The Blind Boy and the Loon
and Other Eskimo Myths

The Blind Boy and the Loon

and Other Eskimo Myths

Ramona Maher

Illustrated

The John Day Company • New York

Library of Congress Catalogue Card Number: 69-14859

PRINTED IN THE UNITED STATES OF AMERICA

DESIGNED BY ROSALIE PETRASH SCHMIDT

For Ramón

For permission to use photographs of artwork on the pages shown, thanks are due to the West Baffin Eskimo Cooperative and the U.S. Department of the Interior, Indian Arts and Crafts Board.

"Loon with Fish," by Eliyah   26
"Caching the Kayak," by Jamasie   37
"Woman with Water Pail," by Ellshushe   44
"Eagle Carrying Man," by Pudlo   70
"Eskimo Girl Juggling," by Pauta   74
"Chasing Geese into Stone Pen," by Jamasie   82–83
"Arctic Scene," by Kenojuak   94–95
"Summer Migration," by Jamasie   101
"Hunters on Sea Ice," by Kiakshuk   108
"Sea Gull with Sea Spirit," by Kenojuak   128
"Owl and Raven," by Kananginak   135
"Moon Spirit," by Johnniebo   156

The twelve illustrations listed above are used with permission of the West Baffin Eskimo Cooperative.

"Fishing," by Nick Wongittilin   18
"Bear," by Nick Wongittilin   23
"Dancer and Drummers," by John Penatac   32
"Feeding Reindeer," by Oscar Sage   49
"Sea Gull," by Oscar Sage   61
"Seal," by John Tingook   77
"Walrus and Seal," by Aloysius Pikonganna   91
"Weasel," by Carl Hank   111
"Reindeer Sled," by Carl Hank   122–23
"Drummer," by Carl Hank   144
"Women," by Nick Wongittilin   147

The eleven prints listed above are used with permission of the U.S. Department of the Interior, Indian Arts and Crafts Board. Those appearing on pages 18, 23, 32, 49, 77, 91, 111, and 144 are works produced in the MDTA Designer-Craftsman Training Project sponsored by the board at Nome, Alaska, in 1964 and 1965.

Preface

The tales and myths in this book have been gathered from Eskimo oral literature of the eastern and western Arctic and Subarctic. They are not the epic hero sagas and legends that are particularly common among the Eskimo of eastern Canada and Greenland. These are stories that were and are used in Eskimo families to entertain the children and to acquaint them with life patterns.

The stories draw on a thoroughly human reserve of emotions, and the emotions of the characters are frankly presented. Motivations are simple. The father in "The Sea Otter Girl" determines to punish his daughter. She, in turn, takes revenge on the men who refuse to rescue her.

The stories do not record or hint at a time when men were omnipotent and had unlimited powers, and as a result of this, a timelessness pervades most Eskimo folktales. There is no hearkening back to a time when a deity set about creating the world, and with one or two exceptions, there is no pantheon of individual creators.

Some Eskimo believe that an Old Woman lives at the bottom of the sea and that she is the source of—and often the creator of—sea mammals. "The Sea Otter Girl" in this book is another version of this story. Animals are sometimes thought to be descended from a woman who married a dog and left her tribe, and a few stories are so common as to be almost creation myths. The sun and moon are believed to be brother and sister, and Raven is considered to be the one who released the daylight. But because of the many different stories explaining one event or phenomena, such as how fog came to be, how a certain constellation appeared in the sky, etc., there is no real concept of a single era when things were created or evolved.

It is impossible to tell when the old wood-carver in "The Man Who Married a Snow Goose" whittled his shavings into a river and they turned into salmon and other fish. This is in contrast with most Indian mythologies, when the people came up out of the earth after a great flood and where a single deity designated rattlesnakes as the bearer of messages and caused rain to fall to help man and his crops.

The peculiarities of some animals are explained by a few tales of fantasy. "The Blind Boy and the Loon" tells why the loon has a ring of white feathers around its neck. In another version of the story Raven and the loon are painting each other black so they can hunt at night without being seen. Raven cleverly leaves some white visible on the loon so that he, all black, will be the most successful hunter at night.

Animals are treated as human beings in the folktales; they plot, talk, and have human virtues and faults. But their actions always retain animal characteristics. Raven is

8

a prime example, of course. He embodies many human failings—greed, deception, and duplicity—along with a trickster's capacity for cunning, a delight in life's games, and a curious amusement regarding all. Raven is often one jump ahead of the other fellow. But he is recognizably a raven, who likes animal guts.

One of the strongest and most frequent themes in Eskimo mythology is the search for food. The weak are sometimes abandoned because they do not contribute food, only consume it, as the brother and sister in "How Thunder and Lightning Came to Be." The grandmother in "The Blind Boy and the Loon" is hungry for tender bear meat, and the girl in "The Moon Husband" longingly recalls the caribou and salmon of her river village.

The Eskimo must constantly fight for existence. With his strength and imagination he must outmaneuver the harsh elements and outwit the animals and the fish, which have their own natural nimbleness and wariness. Sometimes man is successful; sometimes the animal succeeds in outwitting him. Eskimo stories are characterized by a healthy respect for the power and spirit of the various birds and animals and fish.

Some of the Eskimo myths echo themes that are commonplace in stories from other cultures of the world, and yet the Eskimo tales unfold with distinctive touches that reveal the unique character of Eskimo life. The cruel relative, such as the harsh grandmother in "The Blind Boy and the Loon," the monster in "The Man Who Killed the Sea Monster" and "The Hardhearted Rich Man," and the selfish or grasping person in "The Two Men and the Two Dwarfs" are common villains in folktales the world over.

9

Girls are often imprisoned by monsters and must be freed, as in "The Hardhearted Rich Man," and there are certain fabulous races, as dwarfs or giants.

Hero tales are common, and some stories tell of visits by heroes to fabulous tribes of small people or to bird villages. Men strike bargains with bears or sea mammals to feed their villages or are swept by fierce blizzards into strange places.

Orphans are common heroes in Eskimo tales. The orphan is always a poor, brave boy, and we know that he will triumph as long as he remains kind and honest. Perhaps orphans occur frequently in Eskimo folklore because disease and natural hardship shorten life expectancy among these people of the harsh Far North.

Taboos and the breaking of taboos are common themes in world folklore; frequently the human is forbidden to go against the will of the creature from another world. "The Moon Husband" resembles "Beauty and the Beast" in that the wife steals a glance at her husband while he is sleeping. In "The Man Who Married a Snow Goose," the young husband brings disaster upon himself by disobeying one of the rules of the bird village in which he and his wife live. (The snow goose or snow maiden tale, incidentally, has variants in many societies and countries.) In "The Two Men and the Two Dwarfs," the two hunters go against the natural order of the world and are punished by a severe storm.

It is good for children to be aware that people of different cultures and languages have a common ground in folklore. For those of us who are older, who may have dismissed "Cinderella" and "Jack and the Beanstalk" as being the property of children, I hope this book will afford a new perspective on the world of innocence and natural good-ness, the power of evil, and the depth of wonder that myths preserve for us.

Obviously, this book is not a comprehensive collection of Eskimo myths. There is a need for a complete anthology of Eskimo myths, legends, sagas, hero tales, etc., but this book is simply a group of stories that have the most appeal for me.

I have relied on the studies of several ethnologists, anthropologists, folklorists, and explorers to flesh out these tales. Some of them are amalgams from various sources: an incident absent from one variant of the tale is present in another, or motifs and characters from separate variants complete and enrich the main story. In these instances, I have felt free to meld the stories back into a form that seems most complete to me, as a storyteller.

I am grateful to Dorothy Jean Ray, whose knowledge of things pertaining to Eskimo life and art has been an inspi-ration; to Robert G. Hart, Arts and Crafts Board, United States Department of the Interior; and to Mrs. Alma Hous-ton, southern representative of the West Baffin Eskimo Co-operative. Mrs. Houston and Mr. Hart made available for reproduction and use the illustrations that accompany the folktales.

These prints, engravings, and carvings represent work done by modern craftsmen in Alaska and Cape Dorset, and their use of traditional models and subjects, adapted to contemporary materials and art forms, demonstrates that folklore fulfills its promise in the modern world.

Contents

The Blind Boy and the Loon
and Other Eskimo Myths

The Blind Boy and the Loon

Many years ago an old woman lived with her blind grandson in a house built of driftwood and skins. The house was near a big lake. One arm of the lake had five fingers of water, and these fingers held a big ocean in their grasp.

The boy wished he could see this big ocean. He cried sometimes because he was blind and knew he would never see anything.

The boy cried sometimes because he was hungry. His grandmother was old and could not do much hunting. The quick rabbits and owls would never sit still long enough for her to catch them. The two of them ate berries in the summer: serviceberries, blackberries, and soapberries. The boy picked greens in the summer which his grandmother put in a seal-bladder bag. In the middle of winter they had delicious sour greens to eat. Sometimes they netted needlefish in the lake. The boy loved the taste of the tiny needlefish. The old women was lazy, though, and did not keep her nets mended, so most of the fish escaped.

Some years there were many lemmings. Then the grandmother would trap lemmings or try to shoot them with her small bow and arrow. The boy did not like to eat lemmings.

The boy's proudest possession was a large bow and arrows that had belonged to his father. The boy could not see the bow and arrow, but he loved to touch the hard and

curving wood. Sometimes he found scraps of walrus ivory, and he would spend the long evenings carving and polishing new arrows for the bow he had never seen.

One day his grandmother became very angry. It was spring, and there was not much food in the house. "Why do you bother making new arrows for that bow?" the grandmother asked angrily. "Why do you not do something useful? I will show you how to make a snare that will trap ducks or loons."

The boy spent many hours making the snare and decorating it with feathers he had saved.

"Now," said his grandmother, and her voice was harsh, "you will go down to the lake, and you will catch something in the snare. Hide in the bushes until you hear a great rustling in the snare. Then run out and club whatever is in the snare."

"Club it?" asked the boy.

His grandmother jerked him impatiently and pushed him out of the house. "Yes, you foolish boy. Take a rock, and club the duck or loon in the head."

The boy went down to the lake. He put out the snare, and then he hid in the bushes to wait.

He waited for a long time, but nothing happened. He was getting cold, and he wished he could move to make himself warmer. But if he moved, he might frighten away the lake birds.

At last the boy heard a loud splashing at the edge of the water. Something was in his trap! Then he heard the flapping of wings as the bird tried to get away. Then he heard a sad, lonely cluck of despair.

The boy ran to the snare to see what he had caught.

He felt the long, sleek neck. He was careful to keep his fingers out of the way of the bird's strong beak.

"Ah, loon," said the boy. "I have caught you!" He raised the rock to club the bird.

Something warm dropped on his hand. It felt like a tear, the way the boy's own tears felt when they dropped on his hand. The bird was not struggling.

To the boy's amazement and terror, the bird spoke to him. "Boy-Who-Lives-with-the-Old-Woman, let me go. I have a family of young babies. They will starve if I do not get back to them."

"I may starve if I let you go," said the boy. "How good you will taste, fried in seal oil!"

The loon began to cry plaintively. "Please let me go. I will do you a very great favor some day."

"What kind of favor could you do for me?" asked the boy.

"You will see," said the loon. "Please let me go back to my children."

The boy began to feel sorry for the loon. He could feel the beating of her heart in her trembling body. He put aside the rock and whipped the snare loose. "Go on, then," he said. "I will get in big trouble for letting you free. But I know how it is to have no mother."

The loon rose upward in a rush of wings. "Thank you," she sighed, and flew off. Then she returned to circle above him. "Over by the stand of pines, just before you get to your house, you will find a patch of skunk cabbage and wild mushrooms."

The boy heard her fly away again. He broke the snare and dropped it into the water. Then he found the patch of mushrooms and new skunk cabbage. He picked as much as he could carry and took it home.

His grandmother's voice was loud and angry. "Where is the snare? Didn't you catch anything in it?"

The boy held forth the plants he had picked. "I do not know what happened to the snare. I think a big bird must have got trapped in it by mistake. I heard a tremendous snapping, and a big wind went by my ears. The bird must have broken the snare, and it floated away in the lake."

His grandmother hit him. He fell sprawling, the mushrooms flying wildly out of his hands. "That will teach you to be careless! You should have grabbed the big bird before it flew away. No supper for you tonight!"

That night the boy cried to himself before he fell asleep on his poor pile of skins on a sleeping platform. His fingers rubbed his father's bow lovingly. *Perhaps I should have captured the loon*, he thought miserably. But he thought of the mother loon returning to her little ones, and he was glad he had let her go.

The next day his grandmother gave him a piece of dried fish for breakfast. The boy ate it gratefully, although sealskin would have tasted better.

"I am going out to see if I can shoot some lemmings," said the grandmother. She stirred about the house, collecting a bag for the lemmings and her bow and arrow. "Maybe you can make another snare, if you think a big bird will not fly away with another one. Or you can make a basket with that birch bark over there."

When the old woman had gone, the boy went outside.

21

He had a stool made of three crossed walrus tusks and hide, and he liked to sit in the sun. He took the birch bark with him and began weaving a basket.

He had just finished the bottom of the basket when he heard a loud crashing. By the heavy, raspy breathing, he could tell his grandmother was coming. Why was she running? The boy stood up.

"Boy," gasped the grandmother. "Go get your father's bow and arrows, quickly. A mother bear and her two cubs are coming this way!"

The boy was bewildered. "Do not tease me, Grandmother. How should I kill bears with my father's bow and arrows? I cannot see."

The grandmother pushed him into the house. "You spend all winter making points for the arrows! What are they for if not to shoot?"

"But I cannot see," protested the boy. "I shall be killed!"

"Get the bow, and I will tell you where to aim," said the grandmother. You will hold the arrow aimed straight ahead, and when the bears are in front of you, I will tell you to shoot."

The boy scrambled over to the corner behind his sleeping platform. He picked up the bow. How light it was, and yet how strong! He took the bow and arrows.

Muttering about how slow he was, his grandmother led him to the stool where he had been sitting. She pushed him down on it and fitted the bow into his hands.

The boy sat there, an arrow pulled back in the taut string of the bow. He heard the bears thundering about in a thicket. The sounds grew closer.

The grandmother became more and more excited. "Bear

skin!" she chanted gleefully. "Bear grease, and bear meat! Oh, what good luck!"

The sounds grew louder. The boy could hear the low-throated growl of the she-bear.

"Now, now!" screamed the grandmother. "Shoot!"

The boy let fly an arrow. *Whizzz*—it whizzed through the air. With a solid *thwack*, he heard it hit a target. What had happened?

"Another arrow. Another arrow!" shouted the old woman, who was terribly excited. The boy loosed another arrow. He thought it hit something, but he was not sure.

He was relying on his grandmother to tell him what was happening to the arrows, but she was chattering instructions. "This is your last chance. Don't waste it. Aim this arrow straight ahead." She steadied his elbow. "Now, shoot!" Something stopped the third arrow, and he thought he heard a soft grunt.

"Did I hit one, Grandmother?"

"No." The old woman's voice was harsh and angry. "You are of no use whatsoever. We could have had fresh bear meat for dinner. Now I shall have to gather wood for a fire, and if I am lucky, I can still find some lemmings for our dinner. Go back in the house, you worthless boy."

The boy ducked his head and went into the house. He had been so sure that he had hit something with each arrow! Why hadn't he heard the bears crashing away?

He put away the bow and arrows and sat silently.

The sly old grandmother waited until the boy had gone into the house. The boy's arrows had killed the three bears. She took a sharp knife, skinned the bears, and cut up the meat. She put the bear skins on a stretching rack, and she hung up the bear meat on some high poles so it would be safe from wild animals. A small, tender portion of the bear meat, however, she carried into the house with her.

From a cupboard she took two dead lemmings which she had trapped earlier. "I found only two lemmings for our supper," said the grandmother. "Go out and find some mushrooms or berries to add to our meal, if you can. While you are gone, I will cook the lemmings."

Sadly and haltingly, the boy went out of the house and into the woods. Perhaps he could find the place with the skunk cabbage again. He stretched out his arms until they circled a tree trunk; then he sank to the ground and began to crawl around it, searching. If he crawled, he could usually smell the mothy odor of mushrooms or a green and tasty plant.

At last he smelled a bush that had young, tender leaves. He reached for the leaves, to strip them from the bush, and he heard a snapping and rustling. Then he heard the satisfied coo as the leaves disappeared down the gullet of a bird.

"Hello." It was the loon's voice.

The boy sat back on his knees. "Is this the great favor you do me? Stealing leaves from me? Watch out, loon, I might set out another snare for you!"

The loon laughed, a pleasant high humming. "It is time for the favor I promised you. Follow me to the lake."

Wondering, but excited, the boy held onto the feathers of the loon. The bird led him down to the lake.

"What are we going to do?" asked the boy. He heard the water lapping.

There was a scrabbling noise, and the boy heard the loon dragging something up on the shore.

"This is my kayak," said the loon. "Now what is going to happen may seem strange to you, but you must trust me. Do not make a sound until I speak to you. You are to get in the kayak and lie down."

The boy did as the loon had ordered. He stretched out full length, facedown, on the bottom of the stiff skin boat. He felt the loon hop onto his head. The boat eased out into the water.

The boy nearly cried out when the kayak dived below the cold lake water. Just in time he remembered what the loon had said, and he stifled the cry. There seemed to be a long dive; then the kayak emerged. The boy felt the sun on his back.

"Can you see?" asked the loon.

"No," said the boy.

"We will go under again," said the loon. "Do not speak or cry out, I warn you."

The kayak nosed under the water again. The dive seemed longer this time, and the boy's lungs felt near bursting. Lightly, like a bouncing ball, the kayak bobbed to the surface.

"Can you see?" asked the loon a second time.

Joyously, the boy nodded. "I think I see something, loon. Is this seeing? A dim gray and yellow light in front of my eyes?"

"Once more," said the loon.

The kayak submerged into the lake and seemed to glide along the bottom. The boy felt blood beating in his ears. He wanted to scream, but if he did so, his lungs would fill with water. At last the kayak tilted upward. Water streamed away. The boy gulped air gratefully.

"Can you see?" asked the loon.

The boy lifted up his head. The sky—was that what blue was? And yes, that was the way green should be—the grass and the trees that fringed the lake.

The boy's eyes widened. "I can see every blade of grass on that far shore, loon. And I see a lemming running over there, on the tundra, followed by a fox! And in that dark place on the lake, I see a murre diving for a needlefish!"

The kayak touched the shore. The boy got out wonderingly, looking at the blues and greens and browns of the world around him. The loon scurried to catch up with him. He reached down and patted the loon's gray and black head. "Loon, I can see!"

The loon arched its neck like a cat being petted. "Now I want you to go home. Shut your eyes before you go into the house. Don't let your grandmother know that you can see."

"Why not?" asked the boy in surprise.

The loon made a chuckling sound. "You will see. She is planning to give you lemmings for supper, although you killed all three bears and there is bear meat all around."

The boy started home. He did not crawl or walk slowly. For the first time he could see the path and walk on it. But when he got near the cabin, he began to act as if he were still blind. He crept into the house, and he smelled the delicious odor of cooking bear meat.

He saw his grandmother, a tiny, sharp-faced little woman with gray hair. She had a short neck, and she wore a scowl. He pretended not to see her. "Where does this good smell come from, Grandmother?"

The grandmother flew into a rage. "Good smell, indeed! Where would it come from? Do you think maybe you shot a bear and I am cooking it? Not one of your arrows came anywhere near a bear!"

The boy answered her meekly. "I tried to shoot the bears. Do you think you could aim correctly and shoot a bear if you were blind like me?"

"I can do anything," bragged the grandmother.

The boy did not say anything. "I didn't find any plants," he said. "Could I have my dinner of whatever you have cooked? I am very hungry."

The old woman spooned out the two boiled lemmings on the boy's plate and served it to him. With a wooden ladle, she gave herself a huge portion of pink bear meat. The boy and the grandmother sat down at the small table and began to eat.

The boy watched as the grandmother, smiling broadly, cut up her bear meat. She chewed hastily, swallowed, and carved another bite.

The boy glanced down at the lemmings on his own plate.

He was so angry he was shaking all over with rage. He

stood up and seized his grandmother. She dropped her plate and began to yell.

The boy shoved his grandmother onto a walrus hide that was on her sleeping platform.

The grandmother saw that the boy could see. She began to talk coaxingly.

"You want to eat bear meat? I'll give you all the bear meat you want. It was just a joke, those lemmings on your plate."

The boy wrapped her up tightly in the walrus hide. She began to scream, but he carried her to the shore of the lake and threw her, kicking and yelling, into the water.

When the walrus hide floated off the old woman, she bobbed up and down a few times, gray hair plastered over her face. Before the boy's new eyes, she turned into a white whale. A small fish swam by her, and she gulped it down greedily.

Then she swam off. Not once did she look back at her grandson. The boy went back to the house. He served himself a big plate of bear stew and ate it all.

Then he made a necklace of ivory arrowheads and walked down to the shore of the lake. He called to the loon, holding the necklace before him.

Fluttering gray and black, the loon settled down out of the sky. The boy drapped the necklace over the loon's slender throat, and she dived into the water. When she emerged, the white ivory arrow points had become a circlet of white on her feathers.

"I shall be a great hunter," said the boy, "but I shall never hunt loons."

The loon dipped her wings, and raising her white-ringed neck, she flew off to find her children. To her surprise, all

29

her children had white rings around their throats—and this is how the boy, who became a great hunter, knew the loons from other birds and did not kill them.

And in the brain of the white whale are found a few gray hairs which look like the gray hair of an old woman. To explain why the gray hairs are there, the Eskimos tell the story of how the greedy grandmother became a white whale and of how the blind boy became a great hunter.

The Man Who Killed the Sea Monster

On Kodiak Island lived a young man. He was a good hunter and trapper on land, and with his dip net and spear he caught many fish. But most of all, the young man wanted to stand in the front of a kayak with a harpoon when the men of the island went out to the deep water for whales and seals.

The young man spent many long hours practicing with his harpoon. He would harpoon floating logs, and with each throw the harpoon landed, quivering, in the log.

But when the young man went to the old men of the village, to ask whether he could be part of the seal-hunting kayaks, the old men would shake their heads. "No, your father brought bad luck to the village. He harpooned a giant whale, one that was too large for the kayak he was in. The whale pulled the kayak out to sea. Five men of our village were lost."

"I will not be careless," said the young man. Please let me go." He showed them how he could send his harpoon into a target, straight as a sinew.

The old men still shook their heads. "Yes, you are a good hunter, but you would bring us bad luck out on the sea. Hunt bears here on the island with your bow and arrow. In that way you can be of the most service to your village."

The young man did as the elders told him to do: He killed the giant bears that roamed the island. When he took one of the bears back to his village, there was great feasting.

The young man would not be happy at the feast and the ceremonies. More than anything else, he still wanted to be a harpooner in a kayak.

One day the men set out in their kayaks to go after fur seals. Their kayaks did not get out of the bay. The young man and the women and children of the village stood on the shore, watching the kayaks shoot swiftly through the water, back to the village.

"What is wrong?" called the young man.

The women groaned as they saw in one of the kayaks the lifeless-seeming body of a man.

"A monster," the man was muttering. "A whale with the face of a dog!"

One of the rowers told the young man what had happened. "A great fish, almost like a whale, will not let the boats out of the bay. He lashed with his powerful tail fin, and broke up the kayak in which that man was rowing. The harpooner in that boat went under the water, and we never saw him come up again."

A whale with the face of a dog! What could that be? wondered the young man.

The next day, several kayaks ventured out from the village. In less than half an hour the kayaks came nudging back at the shore.

"The whale will not let us get out of the bay," said one of the kayak men. "He means to keep us from harpooning the killer whales or catching the seals."

Each day one or two kayaks went out in the bay to see if they could slip past the whale with the face of a dog. Each day it was useless. The men just sat around the village, in the sweathouse, talking and trying to think of ways to out-was the monster whale.

No one had any ideas. They were all afraid, thought the young man, because they remembered the harpooner who had been lost and the rower whose legs had been paralyzed by the great whale's tail fin.

The young man stood on the highest cliff in the island and looked out to the mouth of the bay. He could see a black object, swimming powerfully around. He saw a spout rise from a blowhole on the creature's back, and he knew it was the monster whale.

"I will come after you, whale," promised the young man. "If I harpoon you, I will be the bravest hunter in the village."

He kept his plan a secret. Dragging his kayak into the trees off the beach, he painted one side of it red. The other side he painted black. With white paint, he painted a crab on the left side of the bow. With yellow paint, he painted a human hand on the right side of the bow. Then he took blue paint and went to the stern of the boat. He painted a blue star on the left side of the stern, and he painted a blue kayak on the right side of the stern.

Then, using a small twig which he broke off a tree as a brush, he painted the same objects on his left hand. He used red paint. He painted a star on his thumb. On the first finger of his left hand he painted a kayak. On the second finger of his left hand he painted a crab, and on his third finger he painted a tiny hand with five fingers.

When the paint had dried, the young man took his harpoon and climbed into the kayak. He sat down on the matting of moss and sticks in the bed of the kayak and began to row. The harpoon lay near him so that he could grasp it quickly.

No one from the village had seen him depart. Out into the bay, farther and farther, the young man rowed. Halfway out, he began to look anxiously for the whale with the face of a dog. It was nowhere in sight.

He kept on rowing. Then the whale rose up beside his kayak, shooting a terrible fountain of water out of the blowhole! The spout was so high it almost hid the sun from sight!

The kayak rocked and almost rolled over, but the young man stood upright and steadied it with his feet. The whale with the face of a dog had made a great circle around the small kayak and was coming toward him, head on. The young man wanted to hide his face from the hideous, red-eyed glare of the great fish.

But he managed to keep his eyes fixed on the whale's eyes. He had the feeling he was safe as long as he kept his gaze fastened directly on the whale.

He began to row slowly back and forth, in front of the whale. First he rowed so that the red side of the kayak faced the monster; then he rowed so that the black side showed.

"Do you see that crab, oh, whale?"

The whale had a voice like the snarling of a hundred dogs. "I see the crab."

"Do you see the human hand, oh, whale?"

"I see the human hand painted on your frail boat," said the whale.

"Do you see the kayak painted on the stern of the boat?" asked the young man.

"Yes," snarled the whale. He made as if to lower his head and charge the kayak.

The young man raised his voice. "Do you see the star painted on the stern of the boat, oh, whale?"

A jet of water came from the blowhole of the whale, as

if he were laughing. "I smash through stars every night, in the water. I shall smash my way through your star also."

"Wait." The young man held up his hand so that the whale could see the same figures painted on it. At the same time, his right hand tightened around the harpoon.

"The crab means that you are powerless against the power of the sea," said the young man bravely. "You are powerless against the power of man—that is the reason for the human hand painted on the boat. You are weak before the power from above—that is the power of the star which I have brought with me."

The eyes of the whale with the face of a dog grew redder. "What is the meaning of the kayak sign?"

"The power of man, the power of the sea, and the power from above—all these can seize and kill you," said the young man. "And the kayak has the power to tow you to land."

With a great bellow, the whale headed for the kayak. With great skill, the young man rowed the craft to one side of the whale as it attacked. As the broad back of the fish passed him, he launched his harpoon into the whale's brain.

Then he held on tightly. The great whale had charged so powerfully that the kayak was being pulled toward shore, towed by the rope of the harpoon which was thrust deep in the whale's body.

The creature crashed on the beach, about a mile from the village. The young man crawled out of his kayak and sloshed ashore to view the monster he had captured. It was a great and ugly creature, with the fangs and face of a dog.

The villagers had felt the shock of the great whale's body

36

as it slid up on the beach. They streamed down the shore to view the monster.

"This looks like the whale that towed your father's boat out to sea," said an old man, who was so old he knew all the village's history.

One of the most respected sea hunters took the young man's harpoon and put it in his kayak, a sign that he was asking the young man to join his crew.

The young man became one of the best and most honored hunters on Kodiak Island. Always, when he went out to hunt seals or whales, his boat was decorated with a crab and a hand on the bow, a star and a kayak on the stern.

All this happened a long time ago. But the Kodiak hunters still rely on good luck from the sea and the heavens and on their skill with the harpoon and kayak. These things bring them home safely, with a good catch.

How Raven Found the Daylight

Many years ago a village stood near the place where two rivers came together. It was never daylight in this village, for there was no sun. The days and the nights ran together in darkness. It was so dark that the men could not see to spear fish or to hunt, so the people were often hungry. It was so dark that when the women went out to gather firewood, they could not see to tell the difference between green wood and dry wood. The women had to lick the wood with their tongues. If their tongues stuck to the branches, the wood was green. If their tongues did not stick to the branches, the wood was dry and had no sap in it.

In a house at the top of the hill near the village there lived a rich man and his daughter. The rich man had a ball of very bright light. It was about the size of a pumpkin, and he kept it hanging from the ceiling on a loop of rope.

The rich man's daughter used to admire her reflection in

the bottom of a tin pot. "How beautiful I am!" she would sigh.

"You should get married," grumbled her father. "I am an old man, and I would like to see grandchildren in my house."

The girl simply laughed. She started combing her hair with an ivory comb, admiring the way the light shone on it.

The rich man shook his head sadly. Then he took his bow and arrows and took down the bright ball of light. He always took the light with him when he went hunting for caribou or musk-ox. Because he had the light to see by, his arrows always found their target.

Some of the men from the village were waiting as the rich man came out, swinging the bright light like a lantern.

"We feel that the time has come for you to share the light with the entire village," said one of the men. "We cannot see to hunt or to fish, and the women cannot see to gather firewood. How much will you sell the light for?"

The rich man held the light more tightly by its rope. The light lit up the entire village and shone up and down the rivers and into the forest beyond. "I will never sell my light," said the rich man. "I plan to leave the light to my grandchildren, if that lazy daughter of mine ever marries."

"I asked your daughter to marry me," said one of the young Eskimos. "She laughed at me."

"She turned me down, too," said another young man.

"Now, look," said one of the older villagers. "Be reasonable, and sell us your light. Our need is great."

"No. I won't sell it," said the rich man, becoming angry. "It belongs to me, to my daughter, and to my grandchildren, if ever I am fortunate enough to have any." Saying this, he retreated back into his house without shooting anything.

The men returned to the village. They were grumbling.

"Why should he and his daughter own the light?" asked one of the men.

"We should steal it from him," said another.

"That is impossible," said one of the young men who had courted the rich man's daughter. "He keeps terrible traps and snares set up in tricky places."

A small boy who had been out trying to trap a fish in the river came running up to the men. "I hear a bidarka coming down the river!" he exclaimed. "But I can't see who is paddling."

All the men rushed to the bank of the river. Sure enough —a soft *swish, slap, swoop*—they heard the sound of a small bidarka coming down the river.

"I am coming to a dark village.
What is this dark village I am coming to?"

These were the words of the song that the person in the bidarka was singing.

Now Raven, as everybody knows, is very tricky. He can shed his coat of black raven feathers whenever he chooses, and he can take on any form he chooses. He prefers to hunt by tricks, and he is very clever about everything he does. He is extremely lazy, and he is greedy. Because his wits are not lazy, he lives very well. Most people like Raven, because he knows many funny stories, and he is a good fellow.

41

One of the old men in the village had seen Raven once before. "It is Raven!" he exclaimed excitedly.

"Raven! Does he really exist?" asked the small boy and the young men, who had only heard some of the many tales about Raven.

The tiny bidarka went *ping-crunch!* as it scraped up onto the riverbank.

The people could only see very dimly, but they saw a large figure, dressed in a rich black coat of feathers, step out of the boat. As he came nearer, they caught a glint of black, mischievous eyes and saw the silhouette of a big beak.

His voice was rather high, and he spoke in short sentences. "It is dark here. Why do you keep it so dark?"

"Oh, Raven," quavered the old man who remembered him. "We do not like the darkness. The rich man on the hill owns the light, he keeps it tied on a length of rope, and he will not share it with us."

"We want to steal it from him," put in another man.

"Or trick it away from him, because he shouldn't have it all to himself," said a young Eskimo.

There was the sound of a beak clacking and feathers whispering together. "A trick, now that interests me," said Raven. "I like tricks."

"Will you help us?" asked the old man hopefully.

"Don't like this dark, indeed," said the black figure that was Raven. He raised a shadowy arm. "I see that house on the hill. A light is in that house. Does the rich man live there?"

"The rich man and his daughter," said one of the young men who had tried to marry the girl. "We thought we could

42

get the light for the village if one of us married her. But she is in love with her own reflection."

"Do you think you can get the light for us?" asked the old man.

Raven hummed and clacked his beak for a while. "I might," he said finally. "I like tricks. I like light, too. If anyone has any presents for me, he can pile them in my bidarka. I like caribou skins, musk-ox hides, food, parkas. I like sealskin pouches. I like ivory snow scrapers."

"If you get the light for us, your bidarka will be full of presents," promised the old man.

"I will get the light for you," promised Raven. He began to climb the hill.

"Be careful," called one of the villagers. "They say there are many traps and snares set up all over the house."

"I will be careful," said Raven.

Now Raven, as everybody knows, is very tricky. He sat down halfway up the hill, by a well, and began to think. "How do I get in the house?" he asked himself. "I surely don't like traps and snares!"

He leaned against the well. "The rich man may have heard of me. I don't dare let him see me as Raven. Who shall I be?"

Then he clacked his beak in satisfaction. "I'll turn into a small leaf. When the rich man's daughter comes to the well with her bucket, a leaf will fall into the water. That leaf will be me!" Then Raven laughed and laughed.

The villagers smiled at one another when they heard him laughing. "Raven will bring us the daylight!" one of the women said.

The rich man's daughter came to the well the next day,

43

carrying her bucket in one hand. She was carrying the light, swinging it carelessly in the other hand. She leaned over the well and studied her reflection in the water.

Finally, she drew a bucket of water and started back for her house.

A small leaf came floating, shilly-shally, dilly-dally, into the water in the bucket.

"I don't want you, leaf," said the girl. With her thumb and forefinger, she pinched out the leaf and threw it away. Then she went into the house and closed and bolted the door.

Raven was not angry. He just chuckled. He always liked games that tested his wits.

The next day when the girl came out to the well to draw a bucket of water, she dawdled awhile, looking at her reflection. As she took the water and was returning to the house, a fluff of eagle down settled into the bucket.

The girl said, "Where are you going, feather? Not into my house!" She plucked the bit of down out of the water and threw it away.

After she had gone back into her house, the eagle feather changed back into Raven.

Raven thought this was fun. He had thought that when he got into the rich man's house, disguised as a leaf or a feather, he would turn into his rightful form and steal the light. But the rich man and his daughter were too smart for that. He would have to get into the house in the water, but then he would have to think of a way to belong there.

The next day when the girl came to the well, Raven was ready. The girl hauled up a bucket of water and started back to her house. Just as she opened the door, Raven quickly curled himself on top of the water in the bucket. This time he was a hair, silver and invisible against the water.

"Did anybody try to steal the light while you were out?" asked the rich man. He took the light from the girl and tied it up again to a ceiling beam. The girl carried the bucket of water to the kitchen and hung it on a nail.

"No, Father," said the girl. She took a dipper from another nail, put it in the bucket, and raised the dipperful of water to her lips. She didn't notice the tiny silver hair that slipped into her mouth and down her throat with the first sip of water.

In the girl's stomach Raven quickly began to grow as a baby.

In a few days the girl woke up, very surprised. By her side lay a naked infant. He was sucking contentedly on a bit of jerky that had been soaked in milk, and there was a mischievous glint in his eyes.

"What is this baby doing here?" asked the girl.

"He was born to you last night, in your sleep," said the rich man. He was beaming. "Now I have a grandson, as I have always wanted."

"He's funny-looking," said the girl. She turned her head to study the child. "Look at that sharp lump in the middle of his forehead."

"What sharp lump?" asked the rich man indignantly. "He's a fine boy. He will grow up to be my helper. Perhaps he will grow up to be a wise man."

Raven, as everybody knows, is very tricky. He chuckled to himself at the thought of the joke he was playing on the rich man and his daughter. To the people, however, it sounded as though their new baby was cooing.

The baby grew very rapidly. Within a week's time he could sit up; in two weeks he was crawling about the house.

The girl noticed something about her son. "He keeps looking at the light," she said.

The baby—who did, indeed, have a sharp lump on his forehead—would stop crawling, sit back, and gaze at the pumpkin-shaped dome of light that was hanging from the ceiling.

When the baby was three weeks old, he was reaching up his hand toward the light.

The rich man and the girl gave him dolls of soft sealskin and bits of bone to play with, but the baby said, "No," and threw these toys away from him.

"Light!" he said, pointing upward. "Light!"

The grandfather knelt down and shook a finger in front of the baby's face. "No. You'll break the light," he explained.

"Light!" the strange baby would cry, kicking his heels and pointing.

"You can't have the light," said his mother. "You're just a baby."

So Raven would cry and cry, and kick his heels, and bang his head on the floor.

He would cry every night, very long and very hard. The sounds of screams filled the cabin. One night the rich man banged his fist on the sleeping platform. "Make that baby be quiet," he said to his daughter. "I haven't had any sleep in two weeks!"

47

The daughter rolled over on her sleeping platform and glared across the room at her father. "You make the baby be quiet," she said. "You wanted a grandson!"

The baby's eyes sparkled mischievously. He kept on yelling and pointing at the light.

"I-want-to-play-with-the-light," said the baby the next day, very distinctly.

"You'll break it," snapped his mother.

"No." The baby looked at his grandfather, who was red-eyed after a night of little sleep. "I-be-great-hunter. I-use-that-light-to-hunt."

The rich man looked very happy. "Maybe we should let him play with the light, if he promises to be careful," he said.

"No," said the baby's mother.

The baby crawled over, very fast, and bit his mother on the leg. She screamed and burst into tears. "Oh, let him play with the light. I don't care."

Very gently, the rich man took the light down from the ceiling, unhooked the rope, and gave it to the baby. The baby smiled over the big globe of light. Then, very carefully, the baby began to toss the light up into the air and catch it. Over and over again he tossed and caught the ball of light.

"At least he's quiet!" said the mother thankfully.

Now Raven, as everybody knows, is very tricky. He played with the ball of light, throwing it up and catching it, then rolling it about the house.

He let his grandfather tie up the ball again after a few hours, and the next day his grandfather gave him the ball the first time he asked for it.

48

When the grandfather had to take the ball of light one day to go out hunting, the baby cried and cried until he came back.

"I want to grow up and go hunting with the light," said the baby.

The grandfather, who had shot two ducks, was very happy. "You will grow up soon, my grandson."

"I am not growing very fast," said the baby. He tossed the ball up and caught it, hiding a big grin.

"Well, stretch, and you will grow faster," said the grandfather.

Raven put the bright light down beside him and began to

stretch. The grandfather was putting away his bow and arrows, and the girl was cleaning the ducks. No one was paying any attention to the baby, who was really Raven, and the ball of light.

Now Raven, as everybody knows, is very tricky. As soon as he saw that no one was paying attention to him, he crept to the door, rolling the ball of light with him. As soon as he reached the door, he leaped upward, released the bolt, and fell outside with the ball.

As soon as he was outside the house, he turned into his raven form. With his beak he broke the ball of light. With one peck of his bill, the ball of light shattered into a million pieces, and there was light everywhere.

Raven flew up, laughing and laughing. He landed on the branch of a tree.

The rich man came out crying, "What have you done, my grandson?"

The rich man's daughter spied Raven in the tree. "That's Raven! All the time Raven was in our house in the form of a baby! I told you that baby was strange-looking!"

The people flocked out of their houses, rubbing their eyes.

"He found the daylight!" exclaimed a small boy.

The rich man's daughter looked up. "Raven, you had better fix that light so that part of the time it will be dark. You know how hard it is to sleep when it is light all the time."

Raven flew up with a long piece of seal gut and trapped some of the daylight in it. He gave this length of daylight to the rich man and his daughter. They took it and went off to the North Pole, and when the rich man goes out hunting with his seal-gut light, people say that is the northern lights flickering in the sky.

As the rich man and his daughter left, without looking back, the villagers were laughing and shouting and running back and forth in joy.

Raven hopped down to his bidarka to look at the presents the grateful people of the village had gathered together for him; food and clothing, tools and useful objects were piled in his boat in abundance.

While the people were preparing a celebration in honor of the daylight, Raven slipped on a coat of bright and shiny black skins that one of the women had made for him. It covered his feathers and was very warm.

Nobody in the village saw as Raven, in his bidarka, floated down the river. He watched the sparkles on the water, and sang a little song he liked:

> "I am leaving a bright village;
> Back there is the village I made bright."

The Cruel Uncle

Many years ago in an Eskimo village lived a cruel man. He was married, but he and his wife could not have any children. Therefore, he hated every child that was born to his brother and his brother's wife. So violently did he hate his brother's children that this cruel uncle had managed to kill the two boys who were his nephews soon after they were born. This cruel uncle believed that he would never die so long as there were no male children in the family to take his place.

The woman who was married to the cruel uncle was made very unhappy by his actions. She went to her sister-in-law.

"My husband believes that if he kills every male child that is born to you and your husband, he will never die. I have told him that this is a wicked, foolish thought, but he will not pay any attention to me."

The sister-in-law began to cry. "What shall we do? I am

going to have another baby, and I know that if it is a boy, he will kill it, too."

The wife of the cruel uncle turned this problem over in her mind. She knew that her husband could never be persuaded to let a boy child live. She thought of several plans, discarding one after the other before she had a brilliant idea.

"I know," said the wife of the cruel uncle. "It is only male children of whom my husband is afraid. If your next child is a boy, dress it like a girl and bring it up like a girl. In that way my husband will not know that the child is really a boy, and he will not harm him."

The sister-in-law kissed the hand of the wife of the cruel uncle. "I will do anything to see that my next son stays alive," she said. "You are very kind and generous."

The wife of the cruel uncle went away, determined not to mention to her husband the fact that his brother's wife was going to have another baby.

In due time the child was born. It was a boy. This news was not given out in the village, however. All that anyone knew was that a new child had been born.

The cruel uncle heard the news, and he paced up and down. "I want you to go to my brother's house and learn whether his new child is a boy or a girl," he said to his wife. "Go, right now, and report back to me within the hour. If it is a boy, I shall have to figure out a way to kill it."

The wife of the cruel uncle knew that the child was a boy. She went away heavyhearted. Within the hour's time she was back.

"Well?" asked the cruel uncle impatiently. "Is it a boy?"

His wife shook her head. "It is a girl."

The uncle waved a hand and relaxed on a bench. "Let her live," he said. "I have no quarrel with any girls that are born in this family."

The wife was relieved, but she was also worried. How long would they be able to keep secret from him the fact that the child was actually a boy?

The wife of the cruel uncle and the boy child's mother dressed the boy in girls' clothing. They treated him as if he were a girl, and they called him by a girl's name. As the boy grew older and played outside, his mother and his aunt told him to copy what the older girls did. Never, never was he to let the girls or anyone else see him undressed, they told him.

The boy was obedient and did as his mother and his aunt ordered him to do.

Occasionally the cruel uncle saw the child of his brother, and he wondered why the little girl was so boyish-looking. Since the child was dressed in long skirts and played with the girls, he never suspected it might be a boy.

One day, however, a strong wind came up. The cruel uncle passed by a group of children who were playing with a ball, and just as he walked past the child he thought was his niece, the wind blew up the child's long skirt.

The uncle saw immediately that the child was not a girl. He knew that he had been tricked and that probably his wife had helped to trick him.

When he reached home, he was in a fearful rage. He called to his wife. She answered his call, trembling, for she heard the wrath in his voice.

"So you have helped my brother's family to fool me. That child is not a girl, but a boy." The cruel uncle was trembling in rage. "I will not be fooled any longer. You go to my brother's house, and you order that girl-who-is-really-a-boy to come here to see me. I want to have a talk with him."

Crying bitterly, the wife of the cruel uncle walked to the home of the nephew and his family. She delivered the message that the cruel uncle wished to have a talk with the boy.

The boy's mother burst into tears, for she knew that the wicked uncle would probably kill her son.

The boy was bewildered, for he was completely unaware of his uncle's cruelty. "Why should I not visit my uncle?" he asked.

Sadly, his aunt told him how the cruel uncle had murdered the boy's brothers. "He is very powerful, though, and you must go visit him, as he asks," said the aunt, sighing.

The boy looked around his house. His aunt and his mother were crying, and his father's eyes were red.

"Good-bye, my son," sobbed his mother, kissing him. "I am sure I will never see you again. He will kill you, as he has killed my other boys."

The boy drew himself sturdily erect. "If you are worried that I shall be killed by my uncle, you may stop worrying. He will never kill me, for I shall outwit him."

His mother only sobbed more loudly and buried her face in her husband's shoulder. She did not believe her son's brave words.

The boy looked around the house. "Did my brothers have any favorite toys?" he asked.

His mother nodded. Walking across the room to a bench, she pulled out from under it an old carved box. "These things belonged to your brothers," she said.

The boy opened the lid of the box. Inside he found the blade part of a knife, some bits of eagle down, and a hard sour berry. The boy took all these things and hid them in his clothing. Then he walked to his uncle's house.

The cruel uncle greeted the boy with exclamations of pleasure. "For a long time I have been wanting to talk with you and get to know you better. A boy and his uncle should be special friends."

The boy nodded, but he did not smile. He was on his guard to see what his uncle might do.

"Why don't you go out into the woods and help me gather firewood?" asked the uncle.

The boy agreed to go help his uncle gather firewood, but he vowed to himself to be on his guard at all times against a trick.

They walked into the woods. The boy spied a dead tree. "This would make good firewood, Uncle. Let's chop up this tree and take the logs back with us."

The cruel uncle barely glanced at the dead tree. "Oh, no, there's much better wood a little farther on."

They walked on, and soon they were walking on a tree-less stretch of marsh. The boy halted. "There is no wood here," he called to his uncle.

The cruel uncle, however, continued walking. "I know there is good firewood to be found in this marsh." He was swinging his ax and whistling, and the boy was beginning to be worried. They were far from the village, and no one would hear his cries if his uncle attacked him.

He followed slowly. He caught up with his uncle, who was standing near a great fallen log. "This will make excellent firewood," said the uncle to the boy. "Do you see any chips of wood that I can use to wedge in the log to make it easier to split?"

The boy looked around and finally found three wedge-shaped pieces of wood.

Lifting his ax, the cruel uncle struck the bleached fallen log a great blow. A crack appeared lengthwise down the log. The boy wedged the blocks of wood into the crack. The uncle brought the ax down on the wedges, one after another, driving them in more deeply and prying apart the split log.

"Ho!" With a strong swing of the ax, the uncle struck one of the wedges, and it fell into the deep crack. The crack in the log was still held apart by the two other wedges. The uncle motioned to his nephew.

"Here, boy, reach down in there and get that wedge. We'll put it in at the other end."

Not suspecting any treachery, the boy reached one hand into the deep cleft in the log to find the wedge. He put one foot on the log to brace himself as he bent over.

"Ha! Now!" cried the cruel uncle. As the boy's fingers closed about the wedge, but before the boy could yank his hand out of the split log, the cruel uncle sent the other wedges flying with two swift strokes of his ax. Instantly the crack, that had been held apart by the two remaining bits of wood, closed together, trapping the boy by one foot and one hand.

"I am caught," said the boy. Then he saw the triumphant, ugly grin on his uncle's face, and he knew that his uncle would not help him.

"Stay here until you starve to death!" said the cruel uncle. Putting his ax over his shoulder, he walked away.

Day turned into night. The boy, trapped awkwardly by one foot and one hand, grew stiff. He began to grow hungry, but there was nothing to eat that he could see. He tried to move, dragging the log, but it was a huge trunk, half-buried in the ground.

What did he have that he could eat? The boy thought of the sour green berry in his clothing. His lips puckered, just thinking of how bitter it would taste. He took out the berry with his free hand and studied it.

Then he had an idea. If the berry would cause his mouth to pucker, would it not do the same thing to the jaws of the log in which he was trapped? The boy crushed the berry between his fingers and began rubbing it back and forth on the inside of the split log. Back and forth he raked the crushed berry. The sour odor that rose in the air made his teeth and tongue ache.

It worked! As if tasting the sour berry, the jaws of the log slowly widened. The boy freed his foot and his hand.

It was daylight before he got back to his village. On the return journey, he had gathered an armload of firewood in the forest. He dumped this load of wood by his uncle's door and knocked and knocked until his uncle opened it.

"I have brought you a week's supply of wood," said the boy.

Surprise and anger were written plainly on his uncle's face for him to read. "Thank you," said the cruel uncle shortly and slammed the door.

The wife of the cruel uncle knew that her husband had tried to kill the boy. "I want you to leave this boy alone," she told him. "You killed his brothers, and I sense that if you harm this boy, you will have bad luck."

"Be quiet!" shouted the uncle. "I will kill him, too!"

The aunt began to weep softly.

The boy sauntered through the village, smiling and waving at everyone, until he reached his home. His mother and father stared at him as though he were a ghost. There were traces of tears on his mother's face, and the boy wiped them away.

"Don't cry. That man will never hurt or kill me. I will always escape from him, in one way or another, and come back to you."

The parents scarcely dared believe that the son, whom they had thought was dead, had returned to them alive and well.

The next morning there was a rap on their door. It was the wife of the cruel uncle. "Your uncle wants to see you again," she murmured to the boy. Her face was swollen with crying.

"Oh, don't go," cried the boy's mother. "Run as far and fast as you can."

The boy tried to reassure his parents. "I told you I would not be fooled so easily a second time. I'll be very careful, and I will be back this evening, I promise."

The cruel uncle met the boy in the center of the village. He was pretending to be friendly and joking, as if yesterday had never been.

"Where are we going, Uncle?" asked the boy.

The uncle squeezed his nephew's shoulders. "Today, my boy, I will show you where to gather all the ducks' eggs you can possibly eat in a month. I know a fine place for gathering eggs, and you are the only person I have ever shown this place to!"

60

The boy thanked his uncle for the honor. All the time he was careful to walk as far away from his uncle as he could get.

They walked to a steep bluff near the village. As they followed the rim of the bluff, the boy saw a great flock of ducks flap into the air. Looking down, he saw their nests.

The boy stopped. "Uncle, I see many nests down there, and they are full of eggs. Let us take this trail, and we can gather all the eggs we will need."

The uncle frowned. "Those are small eggs. I know a place farther on where the eggs are very large and each one has two yellow centers in it."

The boy did not say anything further. He followed his uncle up the rim of the bluff, until they were standing on a high, narrow rock. The uncle pointed. "Have you ever seen so many ducks' eggs in your life? They are all ours."

The boy peered over the high rock. "How shall we get down?"

"There is a trail right there," answered the cruel uncle.

The boy pretended to lean far out to look in the direction his uncle had pointed, but he was very well aware that this was another of his uncle's traps. The boy was ready for this trap. He had seized some of the eagle down that had belonged to his brothers, and he held the feathers between the thumb and forefinger of each hand.

As the boy leaned out to look, the cruel uncle gave him a hard shove. The boy lost his footing and fell off the bluff.

As soon as the uncle saw that the boy had lost his balance and was toppling off the bluff, he started for home. "He will never be able to get back to the village alive," the cruel uncle said to himself with satisfaction.

Unknown to the uncle, the eagle feathers slowed the boy's fall until he was gliding downward. He landed on the ground with only a gentle bump.

The boy gathered all the eggs he could carry, and then he found a path that led around the side of the bluff and back to the village.

When the boy reached his uncle's house, he piled the eggs carefully, then knocked on the door. "Here you are, Uncle. I hope I got enough of those eggs for you. If I didn't get enough, I will go back tomorrow and get some more!"

Laughing and chuckling to himself, the boy went to his own home.

He opened the door and was surprised to see that his parents were crying. "Didn't I tell you that he couldn't kill me?" asked the boy. "No matter where he takes me, I will always find ways to outwit him."

The next morning was like the two mornings that had gone before. The boy's aunt knocked on the door and said that her husband wanted to see him.

The boy again told his mother and father not to worry, and again he went to his uncle's house.

"I want you to go clamming with me today," said the uncle, smiling a false smile. "I know where the shore is thick with large, sweet clams!"

They walked down to the shore. It was ebbtide. There were many clams lying on the beach, and they were large ones—large enough to hold a full-grown man.

The boy pointed to several large specimens. "Let's take these and go back, Uncle."

The uncle laughed at this. "Those are only baby clams. You should see the big ones that are farther on!"

Wondering what trap to expect this time, the boy followed his uncle.

At last they came to a place on the beach where the clams were truly gigantic. The uncle pointed to one of the giant shellfish. "You take that one, and I will get this one over here."

The boy walked toward the giant clam. As soon as he bent over it, the clam swung open its mammoth jaws and swallowed him. It was dark inside the clam, and the boy could feel the soft, squishy foot by which the animal was attached to its shell.

As soon as the cruel uncle had seen the clam swallow his nephew, he walked away, grinning. The boy would soon suffocate inside the giant shellfish, or perhaps the clam would ingest him.

Taking the knife blade that had belonged to his brother out of his clothing, the boy began hacking at the strong muscle which the clam used to open and close its shell. He thrust the knife again and again into the tough mass, and at last the clamshell opened—slowly, slowly, until at last it was open wide enough for him to escape.

The boy gathered a bucketful of the smaller clams and left these on his uncle's doorstep. "I hope these clams are large and juicy enough," he called.

The uncle, upon hearing his nephew's voice, flew into a terrible rage.

He stormed about, getting a saw and some slabs of wood. He began constructing a box, muttering angrily under his breath.

"What are you making?" asked his wife.

"A surprise for my dear nephew," said the cruel uncle.

"Why don't you leave the boy alone?" begged his wife. "He has done nothing to injure you, and I have this feeling that great harm will come to you if you keep trying to kill him."

The cruel uncle ignored her and kept on building the box.

64

The next evening he sent for his nephew.

The boy turned to his mother and father. "This time I may be away a long time, but I will come back to you eventually. Remember that, and do not cry if I do not return this evening."

He went to his uncle's house. "What are we going to do this time?" asked the boy. "Are we going to hunt for firewood, gather ducks' eggs, find clams—"

His uncle waved a protesting hand. "No work tonight, my boy. I have made this box for you as a present. It's a toy, but I think you will enjoy it. Please get inside, so I can see whether it is too small for you."

The boy climbed inside the box.

"I will just close the lid to see whether it will fit the box with you inside." The uncle placed the lid on the box, and then he rapidly knotted a rope around the box.

The boy felt himself being shoved, carried, and pushed in the box. Where was his uncle taking him? he wondered.

Soon he felt the box being lowered, and from the way the box bounced, he knew that his uncle had put him into the sea.

The box drifted and drifted. The boy found himself wishing that the box would be dashed to pieces on a rocky shore or that a large wave would pound it open. But nothing happened. He drifted endlessly, it seemed, becoming hungrier and thirstier with each hour.

He lapsed into unconsciousness, and while he was unconscious, the box was flung ashore by the waves. He was roused by the sound of two girls' voices. They seemed to be arguing.

"I saw the box while we were far up the beach," said one.

"I saw it first; you only said so first," responded the other.

"You don't want to admit that I saw it before you did," said the first girl. "I did, however, and it's mine!"

"All right. Why don't we say that the box is yours, but whatever is inside it belongs to me?"

"Well—all right," said the first girl slowly. "Help me carry it away from the waves, and we shall open it."

The boy felt the box being lifted.

"My, it's heavy," panted the first girl. She sounded as if she were beginning to regret her bargain. "If there are many things inside, it is only fair that you share them with me."

They dropped the box on the sand and began untying it.

The boy smiled at them, stepped out of the box, then fell to the ground. He had fainted from hunger and thirst.

A medicine man treated and roused him. The boy stuffed himself with rabbit and ptarmigan and berries. He saw that he was in a large village.

When the chief of the village came to talk to the boy, the boy asked him many things. "I see that the people here look like eagles. The grown people have white heads and faces, like the old eagles, and the young people have a dark cast to their features, like young eagles."

The chief nodded. "We are eagles, although we can also be humans. When we put on our eagle skins and feathers, we can fly anywhere. You are the first person who is not an eagle to visit our land."

The boy explained to the chief how he happened to be washed ashore in the box.

"Your uncle must be very cruel indeed," said the chief. "Do you want to return to your people?"

The boy shook his head. "Not now. I should never want to return if it were not for my parents. Someday I should like to see how they are."

The chief smiled. "You are welcome to stay with the eagles for as long as you like. I now have another matter to discuss with you. My two daughters discovered the box in which you were washed up on the beach. They are now arguing about which one of them should marry you. Which is your preference?"

The boy tried to remember which girl had seemed the prettier and the kinder. "I think I should marry the girl who said she wanted what was inside the box," he said finally.

Thus the boy married the younger sister and began a life in the land of the eagles. From time to time, though, his eyes would stray over the sea, and his wife knew he was thinking of his parents.

She told her father that her husband was homesick, and the chief called the boy in for a talk.

"Put on my eagle skin and fly to your land and see how your parents are," advised the chief. "You may bring them back here if they seem to be unhappy or suffering. You may even show yourself to them and talk with them."

The boy was glad of the opportunity to visit his parents. He donned the eagle skin and flew the great distance over the water to his land. At last he reached his village. He circled over and over the houses, but not once did he see his parents. No one came near their house, although smoke curled upward from the hole in the roof.

That night the boy, still in the form of an eagle, flew out

above the sea until he found a bowhead whale. He picked up the whale in his powerful claws and dropped it onto the beach of his former village. He knew that the next day all the villagers would come out for a share of the meat.

He perched on a high rock to watch what happened. His cruel uncle was the first person to see the whale. He went around the village, claiming to have captured the whale and towed it to shore. "Everyone may come down for a portion of the meat," announced the uncle.

The boy continued to watch. Late in the morning, when the choicest bits of the whale were gone, his parents came out of their house. They looked thin and miserable. When they appeared on the shore for their share of the whale, the uncle laughed at them and drove them away.

Sadly, the boy's mother and father went back to their house.

The boy was furious. "I can forgive my cruel uncle his attempts to kill me, and perhaps I could even forgive him for killing my two brothers. But I will never forgive him for his unkind treatment of my parents."

Saying this, the boy, still in the form of an eagle, flew away from his perch and toward the crowd on the beach. His uncle was standing near the whale, telling everybody a false story of how he had harpooned the whale. (No one had noticed, of course, that the whale bore no harpoon wounds.) The eagle swooped around the head of the cruel uncle.

The uncle smiled. "He knows what a great hunter I am," he boasted. "That eagle knows that this whale belongs to me, and he is begging for a piece of meat." He threw a piece of raw flesh to the eagle.

The eagle ignored the meat, and it dropped to the ground. The eagle swooped down again, this time coming nearer to his uncle's head. "He wants to get a good view of such a great hunter as I am," said the uncle.

The other villagers, however, began to murmur that the eagle seemed to be an enemy of the uncle's. They backed away from him.

"You'd better watch out!" called a man to the uncle. "That eagle is not begging for meat. He wants to grab you."

The cruel uncle merely laughed. The third time the eagle swooped down over him, its great claws fastened on his shoulders. The villagers gasped as the eagle flew away with the cruel uncle.

"Put me down," begged the cruel uncle. He suspected that this eagle was not truly an eagle.

"I will never forgive you for your cruel actions toward my parents," said the eagle to the man in his claws. "I brought the whale for my parents and for the entire village, but you claimed to have captured the whale and would not give my parents any of the meat."

The cruel uncle gasped and writhed. "Oh, put me down. I will make everything up to you and your parents."

The eagle dropped his uncle far out into the sea. "Swim back," called the eagle. The uncle, however, could not swim and sank into the sea as though his heart were weighted with a heavy stone.

The eagle returned to his parents' house, where he took back his human form. He told them of the box his uncle had made and of how he had been washed ashore to the land of the eagles.

"I want you to come back with me," said the boy.

The parents were proud of their son, and they loved him and wanted to be where he was. They went out of their house. The boy assumed his eagle form and took his father in one claw, his mother in the other claw, and flew back to the land of the eagles.

There they lived and were happy for a very long while.

The Sea Otter Girl

Once there lived on St. Lawrence Island a girl who was beautiful and haughty. Many young men on the island wanted to marry her, but the girl considered each one unworthy of her. She did accept the presents they brought her, however; she was not too proud for that.

One young man gave her black baleen, the whalebone that is very valuable, another gave her a whale tooth carved with beautiful patterns, another gave her soft mukluks for her feet, and another gave her enough sealskins to make a new parka.

Each one of these boys asked her to marry him, but the girl refused. She took the presents first. After the young men departed, she laughed and laughed about all the offers of marriage that she had turned down.

One day her father became very angry. His daughter had just refused to marry the son of a man who was a close family friend.

73

"You think too highly of yourself," said her father sternly. "I will put you in a high place that you will be only too glad to come down from. You will beg the first man who comes by to set you free and marry you."

The girl laughed and tossed her head. "I'll never do that!"

Her father's face was black with anger. He took his daughter to a cliff near the village and tied a piece of thick caribou rawhide to her ankles. He tied the other end of the rawhide rope to a rock on top of the cliff. Then he pushed his daughter over the edge of the cliff, so that she was hanging there, with her head down. He began to walk away.

"Please let me loose!" cried the girl.

The father stopped. "Will you marry the next worthy man who asks you?" he asked.

"No!" shrieked the girl.

And her father hardened his heart against her cries and returned to his house.

Not long after this, the people of the island launched their boats to circle the island and hunt for ducks and other seabirds—auklets, brant, and puffins. The boats steered around the tip of the island, past the cliff where the girl was hanging.

The rope had caused her ankles to rub raw, and she was in great pain. Hope rose in the girl's heart as she glimpsed the first boat. In it was one of the young men she had refused to marry, the whale hunter.

"Come here," called the girl.

The whale hunter looked around in bewilderment, as if wondering where the voice came from.

"See, I am hanging over this cliff. Climb up on that path through the rocks and cut me free. I will marry you, as you once begged me to do."

The young man stopped paddling for a moment. "Why should I marry you? I have another girl I am going to marry." He dipped his paddle in the water and shot out of sight.

Another boat passed. The girl saw it and cried out, "Please! Help me, cut me loose, and I shall marry you!"

The man in the boat paddled nearer to the cliff, and the girl saw with horror that he was the ugliest man on the island.

"Marry you? Why should I marry you, the most wasteful

and extravagant girl on the island?" And on he paddled.

Three more boats passed by, and the girl called out to each man in each boat, making the same promise. But each man in each boat remembered her haughtiness and her pride, and each man refused to cut her loose.

The girl cried. Her head ached terribly, and she was very thirsty. She saw another boat and twisted around on the rope to see who was in it.

In the boat were her father and her uncle. The girl began to swing herself back and forth, pushing herself out from the cliff with her hands, so that the rawhide rope frayed on the brink of the cliff. The rope broke, and the girl dropped like a stone into the water. When she floated to the top of the water, her body had taken on the smooth hide of a sea otter. Using her flippers, she swam toward her father's boat.

Her uncle raised his harpoon, but as he was about to plunge it into her body, the girl raised her face, which was not yet that of a sea otter.

The uncle gasped as he saw her, and his harpoon whizzed past her harmlessly, splashing into the water.

Her father, who was in the stern of the boat, looked up and saw his daughter, who appeared to be floating about in the sea.

"Come up in the kayak," said her father gruffly. "I suppose you have had your lesson and will marry the next man who asks you."

"I have learned my lesson," said the girl, "and now you will have yours. I never want to see you again, and I will never again be your daughter, for you have not treated me as a father should treat his child."

Then her face became wrinkled and black and flat; it was a sea otter face to match her body.

The father began to weep as he saw the wrinkled hide, instead of his daughter's smooth-skinned, lovely face.

The daughter dived under the water and swam underneath the kayak. She upset it, and her father and uncle were left floundering in the cold seawater and trying to swim to shore.

The sea otter girl then swam in the direction in which the other boats had gone, swimming rapidly until she caught up with them. One by one, she upset the small skin umiaks and kayaks.

"Help!" cried the ugly man, who had so rudely refused to marry her. He could not swim and was sinking in his heavy fur parka and mukluks.

"Why should I help you? Did you help me when I begged for help?" asked the sea otter girl. Water separated and flowed off her sleek shoulders as she swam away to-

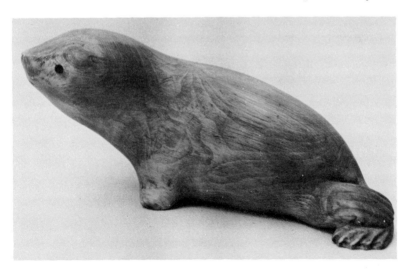

ward the rocks. She never again changed back into a girl.

Many people believe that the first sea otter was a beautiful, proud girl. And sea otters do often linger near the cliffs and rocks, and the bolder ones seem to take a delight in trying to upset the umiaks and kayaks.

The Man Who Married
a Snow Goose

On Kodiak Island there once lived a powerful village chief who kept his only son a prisoner in a moss-chinked log house. The young son was made a prisoner not because his father was cruel, but because an old shaman had once told the father that the boy would meet his death in the ocean. No one knew how the boy was to die in the ocean, not even the shaman. Some people said that the Aleuts, who were fierce hunters and lived on the islands to the west, would kill him and throw his body into the water. Some people said that his kayak would overturn, and he would drown. Some people said a big wave would wash ashore and carry him out to sea.

The chief was afraid for his son, and in order to keep him alive, the chief had the boy shut up in a house. Two men kept guard over him at all times. The boy grew to young manhood in the tiny house, eating food that was cooked and brought to him, seeing only the two guards and his mother, father, and selfish sister.

When these people talked of the water and of the sun, the young man wondered what they meant. The only light he knew was shed by seal-oil lamps. Was the pale-yellow glow that shone through the seal-gut windows really the sun? So the young man grew up, living in the dim little house and wondering what the outside world was like.

Finally, it was the spring of the young man's seventeenth year. He was very restless, and he paced up and down on the earthen floor of his house. He heard the shouts of men who were practicing their marksmanship with bows and arrows. He heard gleeful cries and loud pops as the young boys played with whiplike strands of kelp. He heard the laughter of women and young girls as they roamed about the village.

The young man turned to one of his guards. "I need fresh water. That water you brought me last night was stale. Please go farther inland and get fresh water." The guard departed to do as the young man asked.

After a few moments the young man summoned his other guard. "I am hungry. Please get me some roots to eat. I like those white, crunchy ones." The guards were not supposed to leave the young man alone, but because he was the chief's son, they had to obey him. The second guard took a basket and a digging stick and went to gather roots.

Now the young man was alone! He would see for himself what the world was like outside these thick seal-gut windows. He strode over to the windows and ripped away the translucent golden seal gut. Then he leaned out the tiny window, breathing deeply of the fresh air, his eyes trying to take in everything he saw. The grass was a crisp green, and the sky was a clear blue. The beach was a line of brown sand, strewn with silvery drift logs and dotted here and there with broken white shells! He saw the children racing up and down the beach, swinging the ropes of kelp, and he saw the men practicing with their arrows and playing toss games. In the sunlight an old man was showing two children wonderful figures made with string. How wonderful it all was!

The young man looked out until he saw his guards returning. Then a salty lump of tears filled his throat. He dropped onto the floor below the window and began to cry.

The guards saw each other and realized that the chief's son had been left alone. They rushed into the house and found the chief's son crouched on the floor by the slashed window. His shoulders were heaving with sobs. They carried him to his bed and tried to talk to him, but the young man refused to answer.

The guards were very worried. "What shall we do?" said one guard to the other.

"We must tell his father," said the second guard. He went out to find the young man's father and tell him what had happened.

The chief listened carefully to what the guard had to say. Then he put his face in his hands as though he were thinking long and hard thoughts.

"Perhaps it was unwise of me to keep my son locked in the house," said the chief at last. "I will let him come out, now, and live his life as he wishes."

The chief clapped his hands. He ordered some of the village women to bring a new, soft parka of sea-otter skin

for his son. He told some of the men to place bear skins on the highest point on the island, so that his son could sit there and see everything that was happening. The chief ordered some of the other villagers to bring new hunting implements for his son.

The young man was delighted at the change in his way of life. He liked to wear the sea-otter parka and to walk about the village. He enjoyed sitting with his father and the other village men in the sweat house. He liked to sit on the high rock overlooking the village and the sea. And he enjoyed hunting with the new bows and arrows, harpoons, and knives.

One day the young man saw five white geese fly over his head. He was sitting on the high rock, and his bow and arrows with the ivory tips were on the rock beside him.

"I think I will go shoot one of those geese," he said to himself. He scrambled off the rock and started in pursuit of the geese. They had flown inland, and he knew they were probably going to a small freshwater lake in the center of the island.

The young man began to walk to the freshwater lake. As he was walking there, he heard sharp, excited voices that sounded like girls laughing.

When the young man came to the lake, he looked all around. He didn't see the geese, but at the far end of the lake he saw five beautiful girls splashing and bathing in the water. The young man began circling the lake, ducking under tree branches, to get closer to the girls and ask them if they had seen the five white geese.

As he passed by a cluster of bushes, he saw five white garments of feathers. The feather garments were flung carelessly over the bushes. The young man examined the soft white feathers. He took the smallest of the feather garments and hid behind the bushes to see what would happen.

Soon the five girls came out of the lake. Laughing and squeezing water out of their long hair, they ran to the bushes where they had left their skins.

Soon the four older girls had their feather garments on, and they were strutting around the lake. The smallest and youngest of the geese sisters was looking around frantically for her dress of feathers.

"I know I left it here," she said unhappily, parting the bushes and peering at the ground to see if her garment had fallen down.

"Come on. We must be going," called one of the older geese sisters.

"I can't find my feathers," called back the smallest sister. "I put them here, next to yours, and they are gone!"

The other geese sisters fluttered over to help her. All of them began to look for the missing feather garment. They shuffled about under the bushes, searched the edge of the lake, and flew up into a tree to see if the wind might have carried away the dress of light white feathers.

The garment of feathers was nowhere to be seen.

The youngest goose sister began to cry.

Just then one of the older sisters spied the young man crouched behind the bushes. She began a loud chattering and honking, and the four geese sisters who had their wings and feathers on flew up into the air.

"Oh, come back! cried the youngest sister. "Don't leave me!"

But the four sisters flew away and left her.

The young girl ran up to the young man. "Give me back my skin," she cried. "I must fly away from here with my sisters."

The young man, however, thought he had never seen such a lovely young girl. "No, I do not want you to fly away with your sisters," he said. "I want to marry you and take you to live in my house as my wife."

The four geese were now out of sight. The young girl, seeing that the young man would not give her back her skin of feathers, began to make the best of the situation. The young man was handsome, and his clothes and hunting weapons were of good material and strong.

She went back to the village with the young man. He became her husband, and they moved into his house. The young husband hid his wife's garment of goose feathers, so that she would not be tempted to fly away from him. They were very happy at first. When the young husband went out to hunt, his young wife went with him. She loved to eat the tasty beach grass that grew by the water and the tender, lettuce-soft grass under the trees by the lake. She ate seeds from pods and berries which she picked deftly from bushes. These were the kinds of foods she had learned to like as a snow goose.

In the spring a child was born to this couple: a little boy. The young husband was very happy. His wife would have been happy, too, if it had not been for her husband's cruel sister. This sister-in-law was jealous of her brother's wife, and she did everything she could to make her life miserable.

"Look at her mouth!" The sister-in-law would point to the wife who had been a snow goose. "It's such a funny shape, like a goose's. See how she covers it whenever she laughs!" And the mean sister-in-law would jeer at her brother's wife, until the poor girl was weeping with misery.

One time the young husband was away at sea with his father, the chief. They were hunting seals and walrus in their skin boat.

That day the sister-in-law began abusing the goose wife again. "When she laughs, it sounds as if she is honking, like a goose. It's a good thing she doesn't laugh very often."

The snow goose wife turned to enter her house, for her baby son was crying.

The mean sister-in-law called to two other village women. "Even her baby sounds like a baby goose when he cries!"

The snow goose wife searched all over the house until she found the skin of goose feathers that her husband had hidden from her. Then she took her son in her arms, nestled on the feather garment, and walked with him to the lake in the middle of the island.

Only one person on the island saw a goose fly away from the lake, with a gosling tucked under one wing. This was an old woman. When the young husband returned and began asking around the village to find his wife and son, this old woman mentioned to him that she had seen the goose fly away.

The young husband knew immediately that the goose had been his wife.

He felt very unhappy and lonely, and he decided to set out in search of his wife and son. He dressed for a long, cold journey, and he took with him a stone hatchet, some heavy boots, five dried salmon, and one sour salmon that had been pickled in oil for a year.

He walked for a long time, going eastward. As he was walking up the side of a high mountain, following a very narrow path, he came to a boiling pot in the center of the path. The young man hesitated. He turned to look behind him, but a fierce snowstorm was raging back in the valley from which he had come. He could not go back; he would have to discover a way to get across the pot.

The pot seemed to be boiling by itself; there was no fire lit under it. The young man peered inside. There seemed to be great chunks of meat and boiling fat in the stew. As he watched, the chunks of meat and fat bobbed up and down in the roiling water.

He put on his heavy boots. Looking down through the steam as best he could, he used the chunks of meat and fat to step on and thus get to the other side of the kettle. The meat and fat were slippery, like blocks of rotten ice, and it was all he could manage to keep his footing. At last he was on the other side of the pot, and he skipped nimbly out.

The next day he came upon two fierce bears, who were fighting and snarling in his path. The bears paid no attention to him, but he was afraid that if one bear succeeded in killing the other bear, it would then notice him and attack him.

"Ho, bears," he called.

The bears, their arms on each other's shoulders, turned to him, bloody teeth bared.

"I have some sour salmon for you," said the young husband. He divided the sour salmon into two parts and threw one piece on one side of the path, the other piece on the other side of the path. The bears smelled the delicious sour odor, and they rushed after the fish. The young man quickly ran past them.

He was now almost out of the mountain, except that he had to pass between two cliffs. Just as the young man was about to go between the two rock faces, a bird flew over his head and through the opening.

As the young man watched, horrified, the two halves of the cliff clapped together and killed the bird. Then a fox attempted to run between the cliffs, but the clapping mountains again closed up, killing the fox.

The young man knew he would have to do something to distract the cliffs if he were to pass between them. He made himself a crown of the five fish he had left, and he put his boots on backward. He made his face black with some of the soot that had rubbed off the pot onto his clothes and hands. He flourished his hatchet around and around his head and began walking backward into the passage between the cliffs. (Only, because his boots were on backward, it looked as though he were walking straight ahead.)

He began a strange, loud crying. The cliffs began to rumble together, then stopped. Keeping up the crying chant, the young man continued his backward shuffle between the cliffs. He shook his fishy crown first at one cliff, then at the other. When he had nearly reached the other side, he saw that the cliffs were no longer fooled and were starting to clap together.

With one great backward leap, he jumped out of the way, just in time to escape being crushed by the cliffs.

He stopped to remove the soot from his face, to take off

the crown of salmon, and to put his boots back on properly. Ahead of him, he saw a small house made of tree limbs and stretched animal skins. He went to the house, and when he released the front door flap and went in, he saw an old, fat woman seated on the floor. She was chewing strips of raw-hide.

"May I come in?" asked the young husband.

"If you are a human being, you may enter here. If you are a ghost, stay away," said the old woman.

"I am alive," said the young husband. "I am looking for my wife, who is a snow goose, and for my young son, whom she took away with her. Do you know where I might find them?"

"If you give me half a dried salmon, I will tell you where to find someone who can tell you."

The young man cut one of the dried salmon in half and gave it to her.

She ate it with many grunts of satisfaction, and when she had finished eating, she wiped her mouth and said, "Go in back of this house, and you will see two paths. One leads to the right, and the other goes to the left. You must follow the path on the right. It leads to my brother, who will tell you where you may find your wife and son."

The young man did as the old woman told him. Some distance behind her house he found the two paths, and he took the one that led to the right. For many days he walked and walked on this path. The path seemed to be leading him toward the sea, because he smelled salt air and felt the sea wind. One evening, tired and footsore, as he was following the path, he heard the sound of quiet singing.

The young husband followed the sound of singing onto

90

the beach. There, seated on an old log that projected into the water, he saw an ancient man who was chipping off bits of wood from a large stick.

"Hello," called the young husband. "I was sent this way by an old woman who lives in a skin house near some clapping mountains. Are you her brother?"

The old man kept whittling. "Yes, I am Qayungayung."

As the young husband looked more closely at what the old man was doing, he saw something very strange. The smallest bits of wood that fell into the water turned into king salmon. Some of the larger chips became hooded seals, some of the others turned into bearded seals. The biggest chips turned into walrus.

"I am looking for my wife, who is a snow goose, and for my son. This spring they left my village."

The old man did not say anything; he merely continued to sing and whittle.

The young husband was angry because the old man refused to answer him. He sneaked behind the old man, just as he raised his hatchet to chop off a piece of wood. The young husband snatched away the hatchet.

"Give back my hatchet," said Qayungayung, the old man.

"I will give you your old hatchet, and a new one besides, if you will tell me where I can find my wife and son," said the young man.

"All right," grumbled Qayungayung. As the young man handed him the old hatchet and the new one, Qayungayung spoke. "I am going to chip away a king salmon from this stick. As soon as he falls into the water, you must grab onto him tightly and continue holding on. He will take you to where your wife and son are."

Saying this, Qayungayung stripped off a piece of wood from the stick It fell into the water and quickly became a huge king salmon with silver scales. The young husband seized the fish and held onto the fish behind its gills.

The king salmon darted away through the water. Away they went through strings of kelp and weeds, fighting the wash of waves down to the quiet waters at the bottom of the sea. The young husband could scarcely breathe, but he hung on grimly to the king salmon. At last the salmon left the deeps of the sea and entered shallow water. Soon it was so shallow that the young man was walking along the sandy bottom and trying to maintain his grasp on the heaving fish.

When they were close to the shore, the young husband

looked up. He saw a tiny boy standing there, holding a bow and arrow. The young husband recognized the bow and arrow as the ones he had given to his own son at birth. The young husband ducked under the water and steered the salmon nearer to where the boy was standing. The boy fitted an arrow into his bow, aimed, and shot the salmon.

When the little boy proudly pulled his king salmon out of the water, he was surprised to see the man clinging to the fish.

"Where is your mother?" asked the young man of his son.

"In our house," said the little boy, very surprised.

"Go tell her that I wish to talk with her," said the young man.

The little boy ran to his mother. "There is a man outside by the water who wants to talk with you."

The snow goose wife knew who it must be. She hurried down to the beach and embraced her husband.

"How did you get here?" she asked him fearfully, as they walked toward her house. "This is where the birds come and stay the winter. No humans are allowed here."

"You must let me stay here for just a little while," said the young husband. As they walked through the village, though, he could not help noticing that the people who lived there were of all colors. Some were red, some were white, and some were black, and many of the people were multicolored.

"Do you mean all these people are birds?" asked the husband.

"Shh." The snow goose wife hushed him. "You must not ask questions or be curious about these people."

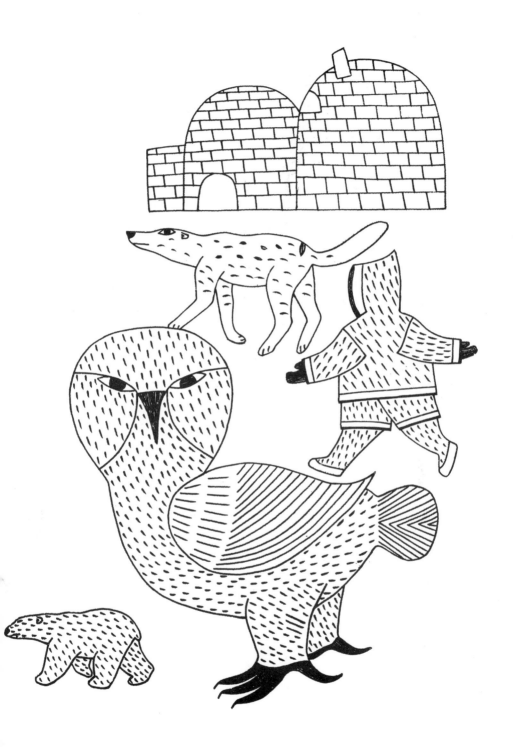

The young husband stayed all the winter with his wife and young son. The four geese sisters of his wife did not like him at all, and they treated him cruelly.

"You should get rid of that husband of yours," they told their youngest sister. "He is not like us, and he will bring us bad luck."

The young goose wife was loyal to her husband, however. She tried to protect him, although there were times she had to fly with her sisters and could not advise him.

Whenever the wife and the young boy had to fly away for the day, the goose wife would make the young husband promise not to leave their house. The young husband obeyed these orders for a few days, but then he began to be impatient and curious. What were those noises—fluttery, soft, chirping noises—that he heard all day long? What went on in the large skin house at the end of the village? Every night, people from the village went into that large barabara and stayed there a long time.

His wife and son sometimes went into the barabara, but they would not tell the young man what went on.

One night the young man could not bear his curiosity any longer. After his wife and her sisters and his son had gone toward the barabara, he slipped out of the house. He crawled through the long grass to the barabara. He found a hole and peeped through it. The inside of the house was very smoky, but gradually his eyes could see through the smoke.

This was the place where the people turned into birds and got fresh, bright feathers! As the young man watched, he saw that there were many colors of rocks inside the barabara. Some of the people were scraping a fine chalklike powder off the rocks and mashing this powder up with water. The people were dressing and painting their bird skins with this fresh paint. Two of the bird people were naked.

As the young man moved around the barabara to find a larger peephole, he stumbled on a rock. As he fell to the ground, he grunted in surprise, and the bird people flocked out of the barabara to see who was there.

"It is your husband!" called one of the geese sisters. Hurriedly the birds finished their dressing and coloring. (In the hubbub the raven was painted black all over and the seagull was painted white all over, and ever since they have remained these colors.)

The young husband and his wife and son went back to their house. The whole village rang with loud scoldings and chatterings.

"Now see what you've done!" exclaimed the snow goose wife. "They are angry with you. Tomorrow every one is leaving this village and moving to another!"

"Let me come, too," begged the young man humbly. "I am sorry I looked inside the barabara when that was forbidden. Please, tell the others that I will never bother them again, if only I may come with you."

The snow goose wife went to talk with her sisters. At first they all refused to allow the young man to accompany them, but the wife begged so very hard and sincerely that they at last agreed.

One of the geese sisters, however, did not want the young husband to accompany the bird people to their new home. She went to the eagle and had a talk with him.

The next day everyone in the village was ready to leave.

97

"I will carry your husband," said the eagle, shouldering through the crowd. Sun gleamed on his white head and fierce beak and eyes.

The snow goose wife was a little afraid. "Oh, I can carry him," she said.

"Oh, no," said the eagle. "You will soon tire, and you might drop him. I am strong."

The snow goose wife finally consented to let the eagle carry her husband.

They were far out over the sea when the eagle swooped down toward the water. Hovering over the water, the eagle bit the young man's arms until he dropped into the waves.

The snow goose wife hovered above the water, crying in distress. But no one came to help her, and her husband never reappeared.

The young boy who was the son of the snow goose and her husband went to a nearby island. He became a puffin, the seabird that nests in rocky places overlooking the sea and straits. The puffin's cry is doleful, and his mate never lays more than a single white egg.

In this way was the shaman's prophecy fulfilled, and the young man met his death in the sea.

How Thunder and Lightning Came to Be

Once, in a summer camp by a river in Alaska, lived a boy of twelve and his ten-year-old sister. Their parents had died during the winter, and the boy was trying very hard to catch enough fish and trap enough birds and foxes to feed himself and his sister.

At night, in their small cabin of logs and grass and moss, they ate the berries the sister had picked during the day. If the boy had caught any fish, they had a splendid meal. Usually, however, there was no fish for dinner, because the older men set their fish wheels turning upstream and caught the fish before they reached the boy's net.

On the nights when they had not had enough to eat, the sister would cry.

"Don't cry," her brother always said. "Tomorrow I will catch an auklet and tie it up on a pole. Other auklets will see it fluttering and will come to the pole. We will have ten auklets for food, tomorrow night!"

99

But the auklets never came, and the boy and his sister had to eat greens or berries. And the greens and berries never filled their stomachs.

The sister would cry again. "How I wish I were a bear! If I were a bear, I would catch three ptarmigan for my dinner."

"I wish I were a seal," her brother would say. "If I were a seal, I would eat my weight in clams!"

They would wrap themselves up more tightly in their stained, stiff caribou skins and play the game. Each one of them said what animal he wished to be and then said what kind of food he would eat if he were that animal.

Talking about food lessened their hunger, and they could then fall asleep.

One morning the sister and brother awoke. The sister laid aside her sleeping skin. "How quiet it is this morning!"

"Yes," said her brother, after listening for a few minutes. "I don't hear dogs barking or children playing." He put his head outside the cabin door and looked around.

"Sister!" he said, and his face was pale and frightened. "They have all gone away. Every one has gone back to the winter village!"

"Without us?" His sister began to cry.

The camp was deserted. The makeshift summer houses looked like empty shells. The fish wheels had been taken down and moved. The drying poles were empty of needle-fish and strips of salmon. The boats that had been turned upside down on the riverbank were gone. And so were all the people who had come to this summer village with the boy and his sister.

100

"Don't worry," said the boy. "Those people didn't want to be bothered with us, but they don't know we won't be a bother to anyone. I will kill a seal, and we will have seal oil and meat for the winter. And when those people come back next summer, guess whom they will find here?"

He was pretending to tell a joke, so his sister tried to laugh. "Whom will they find here, Brother?"

He pretended to bend over with laughter. "They will be expecting to find two heaps of bones in this cabin. But they will find you and me, noisier and fatter and happier than ever!"

The only thing they had to eat during the next two days was a white owl, which they roasted over a fire of moss and sticks. Because they did not have any seal oil for fuel, it took the sister a long while, rubbing two firestones together, to kindle the moss and sticks. The sister then turned the owl over and over above the fire, using a sharpened, peeled stick for a roasting spit.

The owl made a small, stringy dinner.

"It was mostly feathers," said the girl mournfully after she and her brother had eaten.

The sister wrapped herself up in her hard caribou skin, and the brother covered himself up with his skin. They watched the tiny fire die.

The girl started the game.

> "My brother, dear brother,
>   What kind of animal shall we be?
>   Shall we turn into wolves?
>   If we turn into wolves,
>   We can outrace a squirrel;

We can catch it and eat it and eat it!"

The brother thought for a moment. "No, not wolves," he said finally.

The sister sighed. After a moment, she said:

> "My brother, dear brother,
> What kind of animal shall we be?
> Shall we turn into bears?
> If we turn into bears,
> We will have sharp teeth.
> Sharp teeth for eating! Let us be bears!"

The brother was silent for a moment. "No, not bears," he said at length.

The sister fidgeted for a moment. She thought of the splintery piece of owl bone on which she had sucked to try to appease her hunger.

> "Tiny bird bones don't help my big hunger,
> My brother, dear brother.
> Let us turn into birds.
> We won't have to eat much,
> And we'll have beautiful feathers!"

Her brother breathed in and out slowly, as if giving this idea long thought. "No," he sighed gustily. "Not birds."

The game was beginning to help the girl forget her hunger. What could she next suggest they could be?

> "My brother, dear brother,
> Let's be a fish, a bright silver salmon.

Let's be a cod. We can sleep in the river.
We can eat weeds, and never leave the river,
And never be hungry, Oh, let's be fish!"

"No," said her brother, after a pause. "Not fish."
The girl suggested that they turn into walrus, so they could dine on seafood.
"No," said her brother. "Not walrus. Too ugly, and too wrinkled."

"My brother, dear brother,
Let's turn into caribou!"

"No," said her brother. "Not caribou, either."
The girl thought. What could they be, she wondered, so they could be strong, and never hungry, and not have other animals attempting to eat them?

"Tiny bird bones don't help my big hunger,
My brother, dear brother.
Shall we be thunder?
Shall we be lightning?
If you were thunder
And I were lightning,
You could go *boom,*
And I could strike and kill
With my antlers of lightning!"

The girl spoke loudly. "Let us be thunder and lightning!"
"Yes!" said her brother, his voice firm and strong. He

leaped off the floor and began to shake the dried, stiff caribou hide until it rattled.

The sister sprang up and found her firestones. She began striking them together, until sparks flew like tiny barbs of light. They went outside, the boy still shaking the dried skin and the girl striking sparks with her firestones. They continued, until the boy was a booming, muttering noise in the far mountains and the girl was lightning.

Whenever they saw something they wanted to eat, the girl merely flourished her antlers of lightning, thrusting the barbed horns into a bear or a deer or a seal, and they had plenty of food. They were never hungry again.

The sister and brother roamed about the earth, but now and then in the summer, when their people were at the summer camp, they went back. There they caused it to thunder and to lightning and to rain so often that the people decided never again to use this place as a summer village.

The brother and sister are very old now, but they may still be heard: the boy rattling the stiff caribou skin, the girl striking together her pyrite firestones. They visit the earth most often in the summertime.

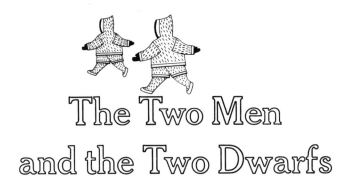

The Two Men
and the Two Dwarfs

Once upon a time in the world there were small land spirits, no bigger than your thumb. These dwarfs looked just like people, except for their size; they were also unlike human beings in that they were magic. These dwarfs were rarely seen by people.

Two men were out hunting on one of the islands where the dwarfs were said to live. When their kayak bumped the shore, they heard a shrill screaming and chattering from the middle of the island. The two hunters looked at each other.

"Do you suppose we have surprised the dwarfs?" said one. "I tell you, I surely would like to catch one of those little men. I would keep him around to amuse me, and when I got tired of him, I would throw him to my dog to eat."

The other man had a kinder heart than his friend. "They say the dwarfs take a terrible revenge if they are harmed

107

or insulted. Let us go find them, but you must not lay a
hand on them."

The first man, the one who thought it would be nice to
trap a dwarf, looked disappointed, but he nodded.

They walked to the center of the island, and they found
small houses made of bark standing in a clearing. The
houses were no bigger than a human hand.

The first man laughed and picked up one of the small bark houses. Inside the house, someone squealed, and there was a tiny mewing sound, like a kitten crying. (Except it was a baby dwarf.)

"Put down the house," said the second hunter.

One of the dwarfs stamped over to the men. "Put down the house immediately!" he ordered. His voice was high-pitched, but perfectly clear. "We don't like people who bother us or our houses, and I promise you there will be trouble if you hurt one of us or damage our property."

The first man just laughed, but he set the house back on the ground.

The second man bent over to talk to the tiny man. "We don't want to make any trouble. We came here to do some hunting, but we will go away if you don't want us here."

The angry expression on the dwarf's face faded somewhat. "Oh, you can stay as long as you don't bother us."

The two hunters built themselves a dugout, which they covered with brush and bark. They went to sleep in their dugout, planning tomorrow's hunt.

Early in the morning, however, they were awakened by the dwarf with whom they had talked the day before. "We found a whale washed up on the beach!" the dwarf chattered excitedly. "There's plenty for you two, if you would like to share our whale."

The two hunters followed the dwarf. On the beach there was a swarm of tiny men, crawling up and over the sides of a silver salmon, hacking off strips of flesh. The women carried these away to dry.

"That isn't a whale!" said the first hunter. "That's a silver salmon!" And he rocked back and forth with laughter.

The second hunter was kinder. "It looks like a good salmon. We should love to have some." With his ulu he cut off a whole side of the fish. He and his friend had a fine breakfast that morning.

A few days later, the dwarf roused the two hunters with a frantic babbling. "We have trapped a bear in a bear hole. He has caught one of our men, and I'm afraid he's killing him. Come help us, please!"

The first hunter grumbled, but the second hunter got up rapidly and followed the dwarf out to a hole in the side of a small hill. All the dwarfs stood about, their bows and arrows and spears aimed at the hole. The second hunter could hear moans coming from inside the hole.

He saw that it was not a bear's den; rather, it was a fox hole. The hunter reached inside. He touched the fox's furry muzzle, clamped his hands around it until the fox dropped the dwarf on which it had been chewing. The man picked up the dwarf and laid him on the ground in front of the hole.

"I'm afraid he's dead," said the man.

All the dwarfs gathered around the body and cried. The hunter then built a fire in front of the fox's hole. When the animal came running out to escape the smoke, the man killed it.

"The bear is dead! He has killed the bear!" All the dwarfs came up to thank the hunter. He felt rather silly, accepting their thanks for having killed a bear when it was only a fox he had killed.

They stayed on the island for two weeks, catching ground squirrels and other foxes and some rabbits. When it was

time to go home, the first hunter persuaded the second hunter that they should each take one of the dwarfs.

"We will be rich," gloated the first hunter. "We can make people pay to come look at the dwarfs!"

At first, the second hunter refused. So persistent was the first hunter, though, that the second hunter finally agreed to steal one of the little men.

They concealed the dwarfs in their hunting shirts, then climbed in the boat and started for home.

The two dwarfs cried and cried, and the second hunter began to be very sorry he had helped in taking the dwarfs away from their island.

He wanted to turn around and take the dwarfs back to their island, but the first hunter said no.

Suddenly and strangely, a great ice storm blew up. The water froze, and the men began to be afraid that their skin boat would be cut in half by the jagged edges of the ice floes.

Shivering, the second hunter pointed out a tiny island off in the distance. "If we can make it to that island, we can build snowhouses for shelter and perhaps survive."

They barely reached the island, and they had to leap out of the boat and pull it to shore, so thick was the ice.

Each man scraped together snow, patted it into blocks, and built himself a shelter from the howling wind and falling snow.

The first hunter came over to the second man's snowhouse. "My dwarf has gone! He escaped somehow."

The second hunter shook his head dolefully. "It was bad luck to steal those dwarfs from their land. We should turn around and take them back."

"In this storm?" scoffed the first hunter.

The next morning, the storm continued. The two hunters huddled together and tried to decide what to do. They were chewing on some dried salmon when a tiny voice shouted in the first hunter's ear. "Bite down, hard!" Surprised, the first hunter bit down hard. Then his teeth were stuck together, and his jaws were frozen. He could not open his mouth.

The second hunter took the dwarf who was his prisoner out of the folds of his hunting shirt. "It was wrong to steal you away from your island. I want you to return home, if you can, and to forgive me, if you can. I meant no harm."

The dwarf stood poised on his opened palm. "I have one thing to say," said the dwarf. "Tonight there will be a terrible wind. You must put your friend in his snowhouse, and then you must pour a bucket of water over your snowhouse before you get in it for the night."

Then the dwarf scampered away.

The second hunter wondered if this were one of the tricks of the dwarfs. Perhaps he should be frozen forever in the snowhouse if he poured water on it before crawling inside it.

The wind began to come up, howling and shrieking like a crazed thing. The second hunter was frightened. He wondered if he would survive this night.

He put his friend in his snowhouse, and then he took a bucket of seawater to his own snowhouse and dumped it over the snow blocks. Then, fearful and shivering, he crawled inside the tiny shelter.

All night long he heard the wind blow strongly and wildly about his snowhouse. He was cold, but he dared not

113

step outside to find wood or twigs. Anyway, this wind would have stripped the very bark from the trees.

When it was daylight, the wind vanished as quickly as it had come. The hunter eased himself out of his snow hut. Only it was not a snow hut any longer; the water he had poured over it had frozen the blocks of snow into solid ice. The ice, in turn, had frozen to the ground. This had saved the second hunter's life.

Everything else on the island was gone. The first hunter was completely vanished; there was not a trace of him or of his snowhouse to be seen.

In a few days the empty kayak drifted to the shore of the island. It was still filled with freshwater and food, as if it had been in some magic harbor during the storm. The hunter climbed into it gratefully and began to row toward his home.

People believed that the storm had made him slightly crazy, so they did not believe him when he talked about the revenge of the dwarfs. And the next time the hunter went to that island, the dwarfs were nowhere to be seen. Never again did they show themselves to humans.

The Hardhearted Rich Man

Once upon a time, in a village by the Noatak River, lived a rich man and his wife. The wife had many ivory hair ornaments, and her boots and leggings were made of the finest baby seal. The rich man had many furs in his house. The head of the harpoon with which he went out on the ice to kill seals was of finest ivory, mounted on a baleen stick. Their cooking pot was always filled with a rich broth in which there were many pieces of meat.

The rich man and his wife had everything they needed to be happy, except one thing: They had no children. They were not bitter because of this, however. The rich man was kind to all the children of the village. Very patiently he helped the small boys to make eider snares, with which to catch small ducks. He carved scrap pieces of orange and white ivory into tiny ducks, so that the children could play

115

the dead duck game. (In the dead duck game, the children would toss out a handful of ivory ducks in a ring. The ducks that fell down were dead. The ducks that landed upright were still alive. Whoever tossed out the most dead ducks won the game.) He played with the children in his house, and for a little while it was filled with their laughter. When it was time for the children to go home, the rich man was always sad. He tried to hide his sadness, though, by laughing a lot and giving them bowls of delicious stew.

One day, when the rich man and the children were playing in the house, the wife decided to empty her trash basket into the garbage heap by the river. She stayed gone a long time. Finally, it was late, so the children went home. The rich man began to worry. Where was his wife?

The night became darker. Still the rich man's wife did not return.

At last he put on his warm boots and went out in the snow to look for her. He could not find her tracks, because many people had gone back and forth that day from the garbage heap.

The rich man knocked on the doors of all the houses in the village, asking whether anyone had seen his wife.

Everywhere he asked, the answer was the same. No one had seen her.

The rich man did not sleep that night. And all the next day he did not eat a mouthful, so distressed was he by the disappearance of his wife. As the days passed he slept very little. He drank a few cups of tea each day, but he still refused to eat.

The house grew dark and cold. When the villagers

knocked at his door, the man would yell at them to go away.

One day a nine-year-old boy, braver than the other children, said, "Let's go ask the rich man if he wants to play ducks with us."

The other children shouted in protest. "The rich man has gone crazy! He won't see anybody since his wife left."

The nine-year-old boy was stubborn. He liked the rich man, and he hated the rich man to be lonely. "Maybe he will let us clean up his house. I am sure the sleeping platform needs to be made up with fresh moss and grass. Perhaps he will let us do that."

Outside the rich man's house the children called to him. They stood in a half circle in front of the house and called, since they were afraid to go closer.

"We came to play games with you!" shouted one of the children.

The door sprang open as if by magic, and the rich man stood there. He was frowning terribly, and he was carrying a big knife. He stepped outside, holding up the knife in a threatening manner.

"Get out of here, you pesky children. I have no time to play!"

Most of the children ran away, screaming. But the nine-year-old boy only backed away until he was far from the shining, terrible knife.

When he spoke, his voice was steady. "We thought you might be lonely, and we thought you might like to see us as we would like to see you. Please do not send us away."

The rich man became very angry. "I don't need your

company. You and your friends must never come back here, do you understand me?"

The rich man picked up a mitten which a little girl had dropped. He threw it out of the yard.

The boy picked up the mitten. Carrying it, he went away sadly. He found the little girl who owned the mitten and gave it to her.

Then the boy went home to his grandmother. They lived at the edge of the village, in a house that was half under the ground, half on top of the ground, supported by whale ribs and chinked with moss. They had lived there as long as the boy could remember. The boy had only two true friends: his grandmother and the rich man. None of the other children could come to his home because his grandmother was supposed to be a witch.

Now, the boy reflected, he had lost one of his true friends.

The boy slept restlessly. It seemed to him that all night long he heard the rich man going up and down the village streets, calling his wife's name.

The next morning his grandmother called to him. "Boy, I want you to go tell that rich man to pay me a visit. I have something important to tell him."

The boy shook his head. "He does not want anyone to come near his house, Grandmother. Yesterday my friends and I went to see him, and he threatened us with his skinning knife and told us to stay away."

The grandmother nodded wisely, as though the snow of her white hair had packed under it the wisdom of a thousand summers. "I know, I know. He is mad with grief because his wife has vanished. But he will not kill you."

The boy still was not sure.

The grandmother stroked the boy's frightened face. "Listen to me; I am old and wise, and my wisdom is greater than any knife. He will not hurt you, but you must stand in front of his house and call loudly. Say this"—and the old woman cupped a gnarled hand around her mouth—" 'The old woman wants you to come to her house.' "

The boy felt that he should obey his grandmother. He went out of his dugout house and walked up the hill to the house of the rich man. He stood in front of the house and called, as his grandmother had told him to do.

"Hello!" His heart was pounding, but he called again bravely. "Hello!"

The door burst open, and the rich man glared out at him. "I told you children to stay away. Why do you bother me? Do you want me to get after you with my seal-skinning knife?"

The boy was terrified, but he did not run away. "My grandmother sent me to ask you to come to our house. She has something to tell you." He looked at the glittering knife. "I was afraid to come here, and I did not want to come. My grandmother says she has to speak with you."

The knife was lowered. Very slowly, the rich man stepped out the door. He was very thin because he had not eaten anything since his wife had vanished.

The boy began to run down the hill. The rich man followed him slowly. At last, they reached the grandmother's dugout at the foot of the hill. The boy darted inside and hid in a corner. The rich man bent aside the skin flap that covered the entrance and went into the poor house.

The grandmother was sitting by a cookpot, stirring something.

119

"Did you want to see me?" asked the rich man.

"Yes," said the old woman. She lifted a spoonful of broth, and a wonderful smell filled the small house. Your wife gave me some caribou meat the last time she came to visit me. I have cooked it, and I thought you might eat some of this good caribou meat since it touched your wife's hands."

The rich man was indeed hungry. Perhaps it would be all right to eat of this caribou meat his wife had given the old woman. He nodded and sat down cross-legged on the bearskin rug that covered the dirt floor. He ate five bowls of the delicious stew, and the crazy look left him. He still looked very sad, but he smiled once at a joke told by the old woman.

Then the rich man began to drowse.

The old woman shook him awake. "You can go to sleep here, but first you have to make a running stick."

The rich man did not know why he had to make a running stick, which is a kind of cane, but he went outside and peeled the bark from an alder branch.

When the rich man returned to the dugout with the peeled alder wand, the old woman said, "Very good. Now you must climb on the roof and place the stick in the roof of the house."

The rich man did as the old woman said. Then he curled up on a deerskin in the corner and slept. He slept for two days, although he did not know it. On the third morning he woke.

He remembered coming to the old woman's house. But what had she wanted to tell him? He smelled the caribou stew, and all of a sudden he was ravenously hungry. He ate two more bowls of it.

After he had eaten all he wanted, the old woman spoke. "Go out and see what has happened to your running stick."

Puzzled, the rich man did as she told him. When he pushed back the skin flap and reentered the house, there was a startled look on his face. "The stick is bent to the north!"

The old woman smiled. "Then you are to travel in that direction, north, to look for your wife. Tonight, before you go to sleep, thrust the stick upright in the ground. Tomorrow morning the stick will be bent, and you must follow the direction it is pointing. And every time you sleep, put the stick into the ground. And when you wake up, follow the direction in which it points. If I am right, the stick will lead you to the place where your wife is."

The man said, "All right, old woman. I shall try to do as you say."

He traveled north all day until he was tired. That night he thrust the stick into the ground near his pile of skins. When he rose the next morning, the stick was bent to the east. The man traveled east, the magic running stick always in his hand. That night, before he fell asleep, he again thrust the stick into the ground. In the morning the stick still leaned to the east, so he continued to travel east.

One morning, when he rose, the top of the stick was curved over, as it it were pointing into the earth. The rich man was disturbed. What did this mean? Perhaps he was very near his beloved wife, but how could he look into the earth to find her?

He gazed about, and directly in front of him he saw a large blue mountain. There was no snow on the mountain.

Green grass and scrub pines grew on its sides, and out of the center of the mountain peak ascended smoke, as if from a smoke hole.

The man walked to the mountain and began to climb it. He walked for a long time, and his legs became very weak. He stopped to rest when he was halfway up the slope. He shaded his eyes to gaze up at the peak of the mountain, and to his surprise he saw that chunks of stone ringed the smoke hole. The top of the mountain looked like an igloo, but an igloo built of blocks of stone instead of blocks of ice.

He forgot his tiredness and climbed up toward the stone igloo. The stones provided a path for him to climb up to the hole in the center. Very quietly and cautiously, he crawled up to the hole and peered through it.

He could not see because of the smoke, so the rich man spit down on the fire until it went out. Then the smoke cleared and he could see.

A woman was scrubbing the floor. As he watched, the woman turned to get more water on her brush of feathers. It was his wife! The rich man almost shouted down to her in his joy. He stopped the words in his mouth just in time. He did not know who might be down there with his wife, and whoever it was might come out and kill him. He had to get his wife's attention without alarming anyone else in the house. How could he do that?

He kept watch through the hole, and his wife continued to scrub the floor, wearily polishing under the table and shelves. The rich man watched and waited until she was on her hands and knees directly under the hole in the roof. Then he spit on her neck.

The wife wiped her neck. Then she craned her neck around to look through the hole in the center of the house. Her dark eyes widened as she saw her husband. He held a finger to his lips, and with his other hand, he pointed toward a door.

His wife smiled and nodded. She quickly finished scrubbing the floor. The rich man watched while she went over to the other room in the stone igloo and talked with a person in that other room.

"I have finished cleaning the floor. Now I will go out and empty the pail."

She came outside and hurried around to the back of the igloo. The husband had slid off the sloping roof, and he was waiting for her. They embraced.

"You are coming back home with me," said the rich man.

His wife looked frightened. "You can't take me now. Old Goose, who stole me away from you, is inside. He will come out to look for me if I do not go back in the house right away."

"I will kill him," said the rich man angrily.

"No, no," His wife wrung her hands. "He is very strong,

with a sharp beak. We will have to use our wits to think faster than he. You hide, my husband. And let us try to think of some way to escape Old Goose."

She hurried back inside the stone igloo, and the rich man hid behind a large boulder on the mountainside.

When the woman went back inside the stone igloo, Old Goose, who owned the mountain and the country around it, was waiting for her. He was very angry, and his feathers were ruffled. His eyes were red and glaring. He thumped toward the rich man's wife on his terrible yellow feet and thrust his terrible yellow beak in her face. "Where have you been for so long a time? You smell like a man. I think you saw your husband out there!"

The rich man's wife was terrified, but she tried to hide her terror. She put away the pail and the feather broom.

"You don't know anything," she laughed. "My husband is far away, in our village. I saw how far our village was when you carried me here, flying through the air very fast. I saw how tired you were when you got here. No man could come to this place on foot."

Old Goose's wife, who was a big, plump woman with feathers but no beak, came out of the other room. "She is right, Old Goose. No man could walk here. Don't be foolish."

Old Goose mumbled, and he shot angry glances at the rich man's wife, but he said nothing else.

The rich man's wife relaxed. While she cooked a meal of ptarmigan and sour greens for Old Goose and his wife, she tried to think of a way to escape. But Old Goose had very sharp ears and a keen sense of smell, and he would know instantly if she opened the door to run away. So

125

Old Goose and his wife and the rich man's wife went to sleep, and all night long the rich man hid behind the boulder on the mountainside.

The next morning Old Goose strutted out of the stone igloo. The rich man's wife poured a bucket of water over his feathers, and Old Goose fluffed them up and washed, making a fearful honking all the time. Then he cleaned his terrible yellow bill on a bush, clacking it and fluffing his feathers. Then he stood still and looked about sharply with his beady red eyes. "I smell a man's smell again. I think you are lying to me. Your husband has come to try to fetch you back."

The rich man's wife laughed and flung the water out of the bucket, making a dozen glittering rainbows. "Last night I washed the collection of ivory charms that my husband gave me. I think his smell is on the charms, and that is causing you all your worry." She held out the ivory charms, and Old Goose looked at them. At last he flapped away on huge white wings.

The rich man watched Old Goose fly away. Then he came out from behind the boulder. He marched boldly into the stone igloo.

His wife was sewing, and Old Goose's wife was eating. Old Goose's wife dropped her bowl when she saw the rich man, and she put her webbed fingers over her eyes.

"Do not kill me," she chattered. "I did not want to steal your wife. It was my husband. He wanted a servant to do the work."

The rich man's wife said, "Do not kill her. She has not been unkind to me."

The rich man hesitated. "You must not tell your husband that I was here."

The goose's wife began to sob. "Oh, go quickly. He can see anything that happens for a thousand miles, and if he is looking this way, he will see you. I will not help him, though. He is an evil being and does many bad things. Run away, and I will not tell him in which direction you have gone."

The rich man and his wife ran out the igloo and down the side of the blue mountain. They traveled homeward for many days, camping on beaches and in abandoned summer hunting cabins. They were about halfway to their village when they heard the sound of great wings rushing through the air after them.

The wife looked around and clutched her husband's arm. "It is Old Goose!" she moaned.

They began to run. The voice of Old Goose boomed after them. "I am coming, and when I catch you, I will kill you!"

The rich man and his wife built a fire, and the wall of flames hid them from Old Goose. They kept on running.

"He has swallowed the flames!" said the wife, looking fearfully over her shoulder.

They had come to a wide river which they could not cross. The sound of Old Goose's wings was very near, a whooshing and a drumming that were deafening. The wife clutched her husband's arm. "Do something, my husband. He has almost caught up with us!"

The rich man thought for a moment. "Give me an ivory bead."

127

The wife reached into the pouch that was tied around her waist and took out two ivory beads. The husband took a bead and breathed on it. Then he threw the bead to the ground. The bead caused a deep well to open in front of them, and the rich man and his wife jumped down into his narrow hole.

Old Goose landed on the ground just as they leaped into the well. They looked up in terror as he stared down into the opening with a red, angry eye. "Come out, or I will peck you to death!"

The rich man and his wife cowered together at the bottom of the well, making themselves as small as possible.

Peck, poke, peck, went the bill of Old Goose.

Fortunately, the well was too deep. Old Goose's bill could not reach the rich man and his wife to harm them.

Then Old Goose began angrily to fan his wings over the well. He created a fierce, wintry wind, and they were terribly cold. Soon, however, he became tired of this. He peered down at them again with a red, hateful eye.

"Just wait. I will do something that will make you sorry you ran from me."

They could not see what Old Goose was doing, but they heard strange noises, like waves on a shore. The rich man boosted his wife up to his shoulders, and she looked out over the top of the well.

"Old Goose is sitting in the middle of the river," said the wife. "Oh! Oh! He is sitting down, and there is no room for the water in the bed of the river. All the water is flooding the land! We shall be drowned!"

She slipped down to stand beside her husband. The rich man handed the other ivory bead to his wife. Again she climbed to his shoulders and threw out the ivory bead.

A wall sprang up, holding the water away from the well. The water was strong, and there was much of it as Old Goose continued to splash up and down in the river.

Gradually the water began to crumble the wall, as if it were a beaver's dam being swept away in the spring flood.

"You had better do something this time," said the rich man.

His wife thought and thought. Water began to spill into the hole, and it swirled about their feet. Outside, Old Goose was honking triumphantly.

Then the wife remembered her father, who lived at the

North Pole, and who was an extremely powerful winter spirit. "I will ask my father's spirit to help us."

She cupped her hands and began to call loudly from the bottom of the well. "Father, my father! Help me and my husband before we are drowned!"

Water rushed and gurgled around their knees now, and they were shivering. The wife called again.

Suddenly, out of the north, the northern lights began to flutter. They whistled shrilly. It became very cold within a minute, and sharp splinters of ice hammered down like nails into the well, because the water was freezing in mid-air.

The rich man and his wife huddled against each other for warmth. The cold north wind blew like sheets of tin slicing through their bones.

"We must get out of this well!" The rich man hoisted his shivering wife to his shoulders, and she gazed out at the wintry earth.

"Old Goose has frozen solidly onto the river!" the wife called happily to her husband. "He can't move, so tightly are his feathers frozen!"

The wife climbed out of the hole and reached down and helped pull her husband out of the icy pit. The wife climbed to a bluff overlooking the river, while the rich man ran down to the riverbank, fitting an arrow into his bow.

Old Goose saw him. "Do not hurt me, little Eskimo."

The rich man said, "Oh, no, Old Goose. I will not hurt you any more than you hurt me." He walked bravely out onto the frozen river until he was standing in front of Old Goose. Old Goose was frozen fast into the river. The rich man shot the goose in one eye with an arrow, so that he was blind in that eye.

"I will shoot out your other eye if you ever bother us again," warned the rich man.

The rich man and his wife went home quickly before the river could thaw and free Old Goose.

The nine-year-old boy saw them coming when they were near the village, and he raced home to tell his grandmother.

"Grandmother! They are back!"

The grandmother went out with the boy to welcome the rich man and his wife home to the village.

The rich man's wife hugged the old woman and thanked her warmly for her help. And the rich man was so grateful that he took the boy to be his own son, and he treated the old woman as though she were his mother. The old woman and the boy came to live in his fine house, and he gave them many good things to eat and wear.

And the rich man began to play again with the children, making seal-bladder balloons for them. These bounced about like lavender beads in the sky.

Old Goose and his wife were never seen again, but many hunters claim to have seen the blue mountain where he lives, with smoke rising out of its center peak. But, just to be safe, none of these hunters ever paid a call on Old Goose!

Raven Fools
His Grandchildren

This all happened when Raven, that tricky big bird, was getting old. Because he was getting old, it wasn't so easy for him to find food anymore. Very often he had to rely on his wits, instead of on his skill, in order to get his dinner. As everyone knows, however, Raven has plenty of wits.

He was walking along the beach near his village, stumping along on his old yellow legs, and trying not to think how hungry he was. He began to sing in his creaky, quarrelsome voice that always seemed to have a note of mockery in it:

> "Here I am, Raven,
> Raven, who found the daylight,
> Taught the people how to make fire and deadfalls.
> Here I am, Raven,

Walking along the beach,
Hungry, on my yellow, wandlike legs.

Oh, I hope my poor, thin legs
Won't break."

Far down the beach he spied the merry blaze of a fire.
He quickened his short, stumpy walk.

"Ah," he sighed with satisfaction. Outlined against the
glow of the fire he saw the ragged black silhouettes of his
raven grandchildren. They were dancing around the fire,
and he was sure they were cooking something. It would
feel good to warm himself by their fire and eat a portion of
whatever it was they were roasting.

"Hello!" shouted Raven. "If it isn't my grandchildren!"

The little ravens stopped dancing and looked at one another.

Raven continued to hobble toward them. "What are you
cooking down there by that romping fire?"

The nine raven grandchildren just shrugged. "We're just
cooking some seaweed," they called back. "You don't need
to walk all this way because we don't have anything to eat."

"Who needs anything to eat?" Raven croaked back. "Do
you think I come to visit you just because I am hungry? As
for food, I know where there is plenty of that."

The nine raven grandchildren exchanged glances again.
Was their tricky old grandfather trying to fool them?

Raven walked stiff-legged up to the fire and rubbed his
wing feathers together in satisfaction. He clacked his beak
and pretended to yawn. "Yes, I know where there is a
great big whale, just washed ashore." He looked at the pot

of boiling water into which his grandchildren had quickly dropped some seaweed. "Whale meat would certainly taste better than this old kelp."

"Where is the whale?" asked the little ravens.

"Around the point," said Raven. "Why don't you children go and butcher that whale and drag the best parts back here? I will stay here and watch the seaweed so that it will cook properly."

The little ravens didn't like that idea. They knew their grandfather's tricky ways too well. "We couldn't find the whale by ourselves. You must lead us to where it is."

"All right," said Raven agreeably. He started forward; then he pitched facedown in the sand. He sat up, clutching a foot. "Oh, my foot," he moaned. "I cut it on that sharp razor-clam shell, and I can't walk." He spread his wing feathers over the foot so his grandchildren could not see it.

"Let me see it," said one of his raven granddaughters, but Raven scooted back in the sand in alarm.

"I never let girls see where I am hurt or cut. Now you children run on and get to that whale before someone else does."

"One of us should stay here," said the oldest grandchild.

Raven shook his head. "No, no, it will take every one of you to carry that whale. I'll be all right."

The raven grandchildren were greedy little birds, so they finally agreed that they all would go after the whale and butcher it. Raven watched until they were rounding the point of land at the far end of the island. Then he flew back to the fire. He took a stick and pushed aside some of the coals.

"Ah," he said with satisfaction. There, in a pit under the coals, was a seal which the raven grandchildren had been roasting. Feeling young again, Raven ate as much of the meat as he could and hid the rest in some bushes. Then he covered the pit with coals again.

At last, he heard the raven grandchildren returning.

"Where's the whale?" he asked them, sounding greatly surprised.

"We didn't find any whale," said the nine raven grandchildren.

Raven went *tut-tut* and *tsk-tsk*. "Someone must have got there ahead of you," he said.

"I don't believe there ever was a whale," said one of the raven grandsons.

Several of them began digging in the coals. Raven stood a few feet away so they couldn't see the grease on his chin. "I think the seaweed is cooked," he said innocently. "And whatever do you expect to find in that pit under the coals?"

The nine raven grandchildren looked at one another. And they were so disappointed by the loss of their dinner that they fell down dead.

The Moon Husband

Did you ever hear the story of the girl who fell in love with the moon? There was such a girl once, and she lived with her mother and father in a moss-chinked cabin on the Noatak River.

This girl always found excuses to go outside at night and look at the moon. In summer, when it was warm enough to sleep outside, she would lie on a pile of skins and gaze at the moon. Everyone always said there was a moon spirit, a man who lived in the moon, and the girl was in love with this man.

"How I wish I could marry the man who lives up there, in the moon," the girl sighed. She was careful, however, not to let her parents hear her speak of her love for the moon man.

In the early evenings the girl would go out to gather fire-wood for the family. Later, after she had done the mend-

139

ing, she would put down her sewing and go out to fetch water.

One night it was freezing and snow was falling in gentle drifts, like ptarmigan feathers. Even though it was cold and snowing, the girl put aside her mending and took the water bucket from its hook.

"Why do you always want to go outside at night?" asked her mother.

The girl was donning her parka. "We need water."

Her father shook his head. "Why do you always want to go outside in the middle of the night to fetch water? We have enough water to last until morning."

The girl only smiled and slipped out the door of the cabin. Snowflakes whirled and danced about the wolverine fur collar of her parka.

Clouds seemed to slide over the frozen face of the moon as the girl glanced toward the sky. She hurried to the well and lowered her bucket down a few feet to the water. When she pulled the bucket back up, she saw that the water was almost frozen. The moon was reflected in the black water in the bucket, and as she watched, the reflection of the moon shivered in the water and then spilled over.

A pale light seemed to stretch and grow tall from the water that had sloshed out of the bucket. Standing before her was a fair and handsome young man. The fur on his parka seemed to be tipped with silver, and there was a silver, translucent look about his face.

"For a long time, now, you have been saying how much you love me," said the young man.

"If you are the moon man, then you know how many

times I have come out at night to talk to you and to beg you to take me to the moon with you," said the girl.

"I have watched and listened to you, and your words made me long to take a wife. I believe that you do love me." He hesitated, seemed to grow sad, and some of the luster surrounding him seemed to dim. "However, my life is a lonely and busy one, and I work very hard and I sleep a long time. Would you be a patient wife?"

The girl nodded eagerly. "I am very patient. As for loneliness, I am sure I could find something to do while you are away at your work." She clasped her hands and stepped toward him. "Oh, do take me to be your wife, moon husband."

"Close your eyes," commanded the young man.

The girl felt her hood fall back, and she was being pulled aloft by her hair. She kept her eyes tightly closed. All around her she felt a great torrent of wind, as if the wind were tugging her back toward the earth and the moon man were pulling her away from the earth and the wind. Higher and higher they went. She could feel drops of moisture on her face, and sudden pellets of ice stung her cheeks, but she kept her eyes closed.

The wind seemed to lessen. They hit a surface of some sort. She walked behind the moon man now, her eyes tightly shut. He opened a door and guided her through. She could see light through her eyelids.

"You may open your eyes now," said the moon man, who was now her husband.

The girl's eyes flew open. They were standing in a big, drafty house. The floor was bare and stony, but it was not cold. Light seemed to shine from opposite corners of the house, from behind seal-gut curtains. These were thick enough so that she could not see through them, but thin enough to allow the bright glow to seep out and illuminate the room.

A caribou roast was turning on a spit at the top of the house. The girl could not see any fire, but the meat was sizzling and browning. Smoke went straight out a smoke hole in the roof and the house was clean and airy.

The girl was hungry, so her husband leaped up and brought down two big slices of the caribou meat. They ate, and as they ate, the moon husband told his wife of the life she would now lead.

"Generally, I stay out all night long," he told her. "Sometimes, though, I have to go out not only at night, but in the morning and evening also. Since you are so patient, my wife, you will not mind, will you?"

"N-no," said the girl, rather doubtfully. She was not really so very patient.

"There will always be meat turning on that spit underneath the roof, and we will eat in the morning and at night, before I go out. While I am gone, you may do anything you like, except"—his voice grew stern—"you may not look behind that curtain—or that curtain." He pointed first to the east and then to the west side of the house. "Those are my business, and what is behind them does not concern you."

The girl smiled. "Yes, my husband."

The husband smiled, too. "How lucky I am to have found such a patient wife!"

Everything was fine for about a month. The girl kept the house clean and made herself some new caribou leggings.

She was very happy for a while and tried not to look at the two shining seal-gut curtains.

Usually the moon husband went out each evening, following a supper of caribou meat, and returned the next morning, tired and sleepy. Sometimes, however, he went out in the very early morning for an hour or two, and sometimes he went out and stayed for a long while on dark days.

When he was home, he was usually sleeping, and the girl began to be angry and upset with him for ignoring her. One morning, as they were eating caribou meat, and the husband was ready to go to bed because he had been out all night, the girl began to whine and scold him.

"What kind of life is this? You go out early in the evening and stay gone all night, and you sleep all day. Where do you go? What you do, and whom do you see? I am sure you see other people and talk to them! There is no one here for *me* to talk to."

The moon husband looked startled, as if his patient wife had just turned into a mad dog and had bit him.

"As for where I go, I go out and do my work. My work is hard and exhausting, and for that reason I need my sleep. And I don't talk to anyone while I am out, for there are no other people here who are like me. Besides, I have no time to waste, or I will get behind."

"If your work is so hard and tiring, why don't you let me help you?" asked the girl.

"My work is too hard for you," said the moon husband. "Why are you causing me all this trouble? I went down to earth and got you, because I had no peace or rest as long as you were down there, mooning about outside at night

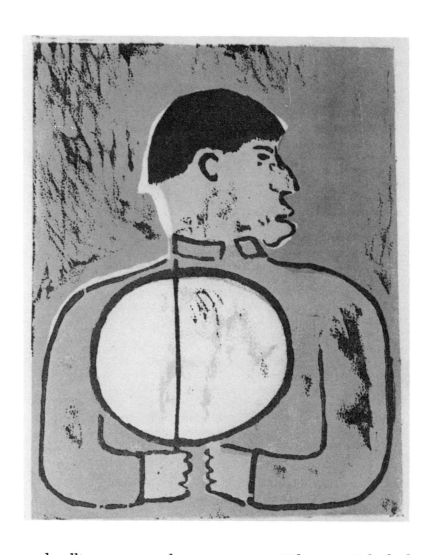

and calling to me and staring at me. Whenever I looked down, there you were, always smiling and staring at me!"

"I still smile at you, but you never notice," quavered the girl. "Well, what do you expect me to do with myself?"

The moon husband patted her on the head with one of

his shining hands. "I expect you to stay home and be a good girl."

The girl began to cry. The moon husband looked worried.

"I can't just sit in this house all night and all day," said the girl. "I begin thinking about my mother and father, and I cry because you did not give me a chance to say good-bye to them." She wiped a tear away. "No, I can't just stay in the house. Can't I just walk around outside by myself? I promise I will not get lost."

The moon husband was sleepy, and his face was growing pale. "You may go any place you like. I want you to do anything that will make you happy." The moon husband yawned. "I think I shall go to bed now."

He went to the sleeping platform, crawled up on the pile of skins, and was soon fast asleep.

This time, however, the girl didn't mind that her husband was asleep. She was going to go exploring!

She donned her parka and started on her walk. The air was thin and darkly blue—almost too dark and too blue to see very well. The girl gazed in every direction, but she saw no other houses. She did find many short trails that seemed to crisscross, start and stop, and zigzag around one another.

The girl began to follow the trails. She was surprised and amazed to see that at the end of each trail was sprawled a tiny man. The man would be lying full-length, on one side, his face to the ground.

The first time she saw one of these tiny men stretched on the ground, the girl had an uncontrollable impulse. She aimed a swift, strong kick at the man.

Immediately, the tiny little man rolled over, squalling, "What did you do that for?"

Fascinated, the girl saw that he had only one bright, shimmering, sparkling eye. "Why are you lying on the ground that way if you don't want to be kicked?"

The tiny man glared. "This is my work. It is very difficult, and you are interrupting and making it harder!" Then he curled back around and fixed his one sparkling eye to a hole in the ground.

The girl followed other trails, and each time she found one of the tiny, one-eyed men, she booted him with her toe, and each time the little man complained and chattered, like a scolding bird.

Once she kicked one of the small men, and he got up with great dignity. "You are a great nuisance. I am going home, as it is time for me to retire." He marched away, and the girl saw that the tiny opening in the ground was free and unattended.

She glanced about. The tiny man with the one shining eye had disappeared and no one was watching her. Quickly, the girl stretched out by the hole in the ground and peered through. She gave a little shriek of surprise. Down below, she saw the village above the beach that was the summer home of her people. The houses were made of skins stretched over whalebone ribs thrust upright into the ground.

As the girl looked more closely, she saw her father's kayak out on the sea. His harpoon was upraised, and as she watched, he flung it at a seal.

The girl's attention returned to the village. In the scrub-

146

by bushes behind the village, she spied a familiar parka. It was her mother! The girl had to clap one hand over her mouth to keep from crying aloud in welcome and delight. A sealskin poke dangled from one of her mother's arms, and the mother was picking berries and popping them into the poke. As the girl watched, her mother began walking

back toward the summer village toward one of the skin-covered dugouts. Passing a rack of drying split salmon, the mother entered one of the dugouts.

The girl waited a moment, but her mother did not reappear. The drying salmon swayed in the breeze, and the girl thought how hungry she was for salmon and how tired she was of caribou meat.

The girl scrambled up from the opening in the ground and ran home. As she ran, she managed to kick one or two of the small, one-eyed men, who leaped with surprise as she passed.

The moon husband was still asleep when the girl reached their house. His breathing was loud and regular.

The girl sat down in the middle of the house and began to cry. She was getting tired of this place. How nice it would be to go home for a visit, to eat salmon and to joke with her mother.

Through her tears, the girl saw the seal-gut curtain at the east end of the house glow and shimmer. She cast a quick look at the moon husband. Good, he was still sleeping! Surely it could not do much harm if she were merely to peek behind the curtain.

The girl's tears dried. She tiptoed over to the bright curtain at the east side of the house. With a quick fling, she tossed aside the curtain. Her breath came out in a long sigh. There lay a half-moon, a quarter moon, and a small sliver of a moon. So this was her husband's secret! He was the man who carried the moon about the sky at night, and he kept behind these curtains the various phases of the moon!

The girl ran to the seal-gut curtain at the west side of the house and flung it back. The shining became so bright it hurt her eyes. Behind this curtain she found a full moon, one that was almost full, and another that was slightly more than half full.

The girl liked best the moon that was almost full. She looked over one shoulder at her husband. He was still sleeping soundly. She looked back at the moons. Surely it could not cause any harm to anyone if she were just to try one on for a moment, to see how it looked on her.

The girl's hand slipped forth, and she grasped the moon that was almost full. To her surprise, it was cool and bright, not at all hot. She put it to her face. The moon was just about the size of her own face, and it fit nicely. It was fun to carry this bright glow wherever she went, to shine this light everywhere she turned!

All of a sudden the moon face began to sting. It stung the girl's face until it felt like a thousand burning nettles. She tried to pull the moon off, but it was stuck fast. The harder she pulled, the more stubbornly did the moon cling to her nose and cheeks. The stinging was terrible!

"Ay, ay, yay, hay, oh, ay," moaned the girl, trying desperately to pull away the clinging moon face. It was no use; the moon was stuck fast.

The girl was afraid to rouse her husband and tell him what had happened. He would be very angry with her if he knew that she had disobeyed his instructions never to look behind the seal-gut curtains.

She heard her husband stir and mumble, as if he were just waking up.

149

The girl raced to the sleeping platform and covered herself up with a heap of caribou skins.

Her husband sat up. "Get up, wife. I am hungry for my supper."

"I'm not hungry," said the girl. "Go ahead, and eat by yourself." Then a groan escaped her lips. "Oh, how my face hurts!"

"Let me rub it for you," said the moon husband.

The girl was still bundled under the skins, and her voice was muffled. "No, I will just lie here. Perhaps the pain will go away."

The husband suspected that his wife had looked behind the curtains, but he wanted her to tell him what she had done.

"What did you do today?" he asked.

"Oh, I just walked around," said the girl.

"Did you see anyone?" asked the moon husband.

The girl giggled, forgetting her pain for a moment. "I saw many funny, tiny men. They all were stretched out on the ground, looking through holes toward earth. They looked so funny, lying there like that, that I kicked each one as I went past him!" The girl laughed. "And when each one of these little men looked up to scold me, I saw that he had only one eye!"

"Those were stars," said the moon husband. He was dismayed and angered by what his wife had done. "You should not have kicked them!"

The girl paid no attention to him. "I also saw my mother and father. My father was out in his boat, harpooning a seal, and my mother was gathering berries near the summer village. How sad they looked!" She wept quietly for a moment. "I wish I could go back for a visit. I would tell them I am all right so they would not worry."

The moon husband went toward the east curtain while his wife was talking. He suspected the real reason for the pain on his wife's face, and he was going to investigate to see if he was right. Although this curtain was slightly disarranged, there was nothing missing.

The husband went toward the west side of the house. The translucent seal-gut curtain was pulled to one side. The husband held it back in order to count the moons behind it. There was the full moon, and there was the moon that was more than half full. But where was the moon that was almost full?

The girl was still talking. "Could we go back to visit my parents? I should like to see them. I get so bored here. There is nothing to do, and you do not even want me to kick the tiny, one-eyed men!"

The husband threw back the pile of skins covering the girl. He saw the moon that was almost full, clinging to her face.

"Why did you look behind the curtains?" he asked. "Didn't I forbid you to do that?"

The girl began to cry, and the tears slithered from behind the moon mask. "I tried it on for fun, and now it is stuck, and I can't take it off!"

The moon husband gently reached toward her and pried loose the moon from the girl's face. It came off easily.

"We shall go visit your parents next week," said the moon husband to his wife. "Now will you be good?"

151

By the time the moon husband and his wife left to go down to earth, the girl's family had returned to their winter cabin.

"Why are we taking a dogsled?" asked the girl as they climbed into a sled with high and shining whalebone runners. The six dogs that were hitched to the sled were prancing up and down, as if they were eager to be off. "You did not use a sled to bring me up here."

"We need the sled to take these presents of caribou meat and skins to your parents," said the moon husband.

The girl believed him. The moon husband took the reins, called to the snarling dogs, and the sled leaped out into the sky.

After a long journey, they reached the moss-chinked cabin where the girl had lived before she married the man from the moon. The husband unhitched the dogs and tied them to a pole, and they began growling and fighting among themselves. He threw them each a large hunk of caribou meat, which quieted them.

"You must go to the door first," said the moon man to his wife. "Tell your mother she must hang a curtain of split, sewn-together seal intestines in front of one corner. Then your mother and father must hide their eyes while I go behind that curtain. They must never see my face."

The girl was disappointed, for she thought her husband was very handsome, and she would have liked her parents to see him. However, she had to do as he said.

While the moon husband hid behind the food cache, the daughter knocked at the door of her parents' cabin.

The door was opened by the girl's mother. The mother's face grew white when she saw who was standing there, for she had thought her daughter had drowned or been eaten by wolves.

"It is I—your daughter," said the girl quickly. "My husband and I have come back to visit you."

The girl's father came to the door. They drew her inside and embraced her. At last the girl pulled away from her parents.

"My husband is waiting outside, and he cannot come in until you have made us a bed in the corner of skins and have hung a curtain of seal guts in front of the corner. When you have hung the curtain, both of you must hide your faces, for you may not look upon my husband."

"What kind of husband is this?" said the father angrily.

"I have married the man from the moon, Father, and it is his law that no one shall see him but me."

"Is he so ugly?" asked the mother.

The girl was indignant, for her husband was not ugly. He was very handsome. "He just does not like to be stared at all the time," said the girl. "Now, Mother, let me help you hang up the curtain."

Using some hooks, the mother and daughter strung up the seal-gut curtain. They made a bed of furs and skins behind the curtain.

"Now," said the girl, "you must turn your faces to the wall, and I will bring in my husband and put him behind the curtain."

The parents obeyed their daughter. They heard a rush of wind as the door opened; then it was closed. They heard footsteps which carried the moon husband across the room and into the corner behind the seal-gut curtain.

In a few moments their daughter came out from behind

the curtain. She was carrying the wet clothing which her husband had been wearing. Snow lay heavy and wet between the inner and outer layers of the garments. The mother quickly beat and brushed out the snow and hung the clothing up to dry.

"We came through a great snowstorm on the way here," said the moon husband from behind the golden curtain.

"Have you come far?" asked the girl's father.

"Very far," said the moon man. "I am empty with hunger."

"What would you like?" asked his mother-in-law.

The girl interrupted. "I would like some dried meat that has soaked a long time in seal oil. Or some dried salmon. Where we live, we always eat caribou. All the time, caribou."

"I like caribou," said the girl's mother.

The girl laughed. "We brought you great quantities of caribou meat and skins. Mother, I will heat some caribou meat in melted tallow for you and father, if you will fix some fish for me and my husband."

So the two women fixed the meal, while the moon husband stayed behind the seal-gut curtain and talked to his father-in-law. When the meal was ready, the girl took two plates of fish behind the curtain to eat with her husband. The mother and father feasted on dried caribou in front of the curtain.

"You must stay for a while," said the mother to her daughter's husband. "We will make whalebone runners for your sled, and my daughter and I will sew sealskin parkas and leggings for you." The mother wondered what

154

her daughter's husband looked like. His shadow on the curtain was very handsome.

"Let's do stay for a few days," the girl begged her husband. "I get so hungry on the moon, for we have no fish or seal meat there. I am so tired of eating caribou."

The the daughter squealed with delight, for her mother handed dessert around the curtain. The dessert was a kind of ice cream made of frozen seal oil and crushed berries, flavored with a little sugar. The girl fed her husband a bite of the seal-oil ice cream. "Isn't that better than anything we've had on the moon?" she asked joyfully.

The moon husband agreed to stay with his wife's family for a few days. During that time he slept a great deal behind the curtain, while his wife and her mother chewed sealskin to make ropes and mittens.

The girl's mother was very curious to see her daughter's husband. "Is he handsome?" she would ask, and when her daughter said yes, the mother refused to believe her. "If he is so good-looking, why is he afraid to show his face?"

At last the girl could stand her mother's teasing no longer. She took a seal-oil lamp and trimmed off the dead moss so that it would burn more brightly. She motioned her mother over to the seal-gut curtain. Shoving aside the golden, thick curtain, the girl held the seal-oil lamp high over the moon husband's face so that her mother could see him.

The mother gazed with awe and pleasure at the beautiful young man whom her daughter had married. His face was peaceful, and his skin was so fair that it seemed to glow like fog over sunlight.

"He is indeed handsome," whispered the mother.

"I told you so," said the girl triumphantly.

Just then a bit of dried, blazing moss broke off the wick of the lamp and fell onto the moon husband. The spark landed on his neck, and he leaped up off his bed of animal hides.

He saw his wife standing there, the seal-oil lamp raised high above her, and he saw the guilty look on the face of his mother-in-law as she backed away from him.

"You could not even obey me in this," said the moon husband sorrowfully. "I told you that I needed a patient, untroublesome wife, and you give me nothing but trouble. I told you not to look behind the seal-gut curtains at our home, and you not only looked behind them, but you stole one of my moons to put on your face. You kicked the stars, from a pure wish to make mischief, I suppose.

"Now we come to the home of your parents, because you begged me to let you return for a visit. I agreed to bring you here and asked only that you keep my face hidden from the sight of your mother and father. This is the last time you will have a chance to disobey me." Saying this, the moon husband sprang out the door. The girl and her mother ran after him, just in time to see him vanish upward in the air. There was a rushing of wind and a burst of light.

The moon, which had been absent from the sky for a few days, was back in place.

The girl began to weep. "Why did you tease me to show you my husband's face?" she asked her mother over and over. At night the girl went out into the cold and stood staring up at the moon, begging him to come back for her.

She fed and took care of her husband's dogs and dogsled, which he had left behind. In case he returned for her, everything would be in good order. She mended the harnesses and lines, which were made of caribou hide. She polished the new whalebone runners which her father had made. But the moon took no notice of any of these things or of her.

"I am so sorry," the girl called over and over to the moon's face as it changed from a sliver to a quarter phase and to half full. "I would do anything to be near you. I would even be one of those foolish stars."

But the moon paid no heed.

One night, when the moon was full and bright, the girl's father came rushing into the house. "I saw a bear down the river. He seemed tired and sluggish, and I know I can shoot him. Let us take the dogsled and go after him."

157

The girl had not let her father touch the sled since her husband left, but this time she agreed. She would drive the sled while her father looked for the bear to shoot it.

The dogs barked and whined, in a frenzy of activity. She harnessed them while her father got together his hunting weapons. Then the girl and her father climbed into the sled. The whalebone runners fairly flew over the frozen ground.

"Wait!" cried the father. "Stop for a moment. I forgot my mittens, and my hands will freeze if I do not get them."

The girl pulled on the reins until the eager dogs came to a stop. Her father climbed out of the sled and ran toward the cabin. He heard a whizzing noise behind him and turned around. The sled was racing over the ground, fast and then faster.

"Stop!" called the father. He ran after the sled, waving his arms. "Stop!"

But the sled did not stop; the dogs, their fur silver and shining, seemed to leap off the ground. The sled followed the dogs, which were running nimbly over the blue tundra of the sky. The father could see his daughter in the sled. She turned once and waved to him.

He watched the sled until it turned into blazing pinpoints of light in the night sky. The six dogs and the girl and the sled had become those seven stars that are known as the Pleiades. Every night they are visible in the sky, heading toward the moon.

Glossary

BALEEN. A horny substance, like bone, that grows in the mouths of whales.

BARABARA. A sod or turf hut built wholly or partly underground.

BIDARKA. A light boat of skins stretched over a light wooden frame.

DEADFALL. A kind of trap constructed so that a weight falls, killing or stunning the animal caught in it.

EIDER. A large sea duck found in the north.

FLENSE. To strip a carcass of blubber or skin. Usually refers to whale or seal.

HARPOON. A barbed spear with a triangular head on a long shaft.

KAYAK. A closed-in Eskimo skin canoe with a circular hole through which the oarsman slides his legs and sits upright.

LEMMING. A small rodent.

MUKLUKS. Sealskin or reindeer-skin boots.

MURRE. A kind of auk.

PARKA. A hooded pullover outer garment that reaches to the thighs or knees. It is usually made of hides and lined with wolverine fur.

PTARMIGAN. A northern grouse that is completely white in winter.

SHAMAN. A medicine man, a priest-doctor.

SWEATHOUSE. A hut heated by steam and used for therapeutic or ceremonial purposes.

TUNDRA. A level or gently rolling treeless plain above the Arctic Circle.

ULU. Skinning knife used by Eskimo women. It has a crescent-shaped blade.

UMIAK. An open Eskimo boat made of a wooden frame covered with hides.

About the Author

RAMONA MAHER's previous books include two novels for young readers, *A Dime for Romance* and *Their Shining Hour,* and two nonfiction books: *Shifting Sands, The Story of Sand Dunes,* and *Ice Island,* concerning polar science and the Arctic Research Laboratory, on which she collaborated with her husband. It was while she and her husband were living in Alaska that Ramona Maher first became interested in the Eskimo myths.